D0365457

THE UNCLEAN SKY

LOUIS J. BATTAN was born in 1923 in New York City. After having entered City College of New York, he enlisted in the U. S. Army Air Force in World War II. As an Air Force lieutenant he studied electronics and radar at Harvard and M.I.T. Following the war he continued his studies, receiving a B.S. degree in 1946 from New York University and an M.S. in 1949 and Ph.D. in 1953 at the University of Chicago. During the period 1947 to 1950 he was employed as a research meteorologist for the U. S. Weather Bureau and from 1950 to 1958 was associated with the University of Chicago as a research associate and staff meteorologist.

In 1958, Dr. Battan joined the faculty of the University of Arizona as a Professor of Meteorology and Associate Director of the Institute of Atmospheric Physics. Since then he has continued to do research in various areas of physical meteorology. In 1962 he received the Meisinger Award of the American Meteorological Society for Research Achievements. He has served that Society as a member of its Council in 1959–61, as a member of many committees and is currently its president. He has acted as a consultant to the National Science Foundation, U. S. Weather Bureau, Air Force, Army, and National Institutes of Health.

Professor Battan is an associate editor of the *Journal of Atmospheric Sciences*. He has written many articles for scientific and technical publications as well as for a number of encyclopedias. He is the author of a number of books: *Radar Meteorology* (University of Chicago Press, 1959), co-author of *Earth and Space Science* (D. C. Heath, 1966), *The Thunderstorm* (New American Library, 1964). This is his fourth book for the Science Study Series, the previous ones being *The Nature of Violent Storms* (1961), *Radar Observes the Weather* (1962), and *Cloud Physics and Cloud Seeding* (1962).

THE UNCLEAN SKY

A meteorologist looks at air pollution

LOUIS J. BATTAN

ILLUSTRATIONS BY THE AUTHOR
AND D. C. PERCENY

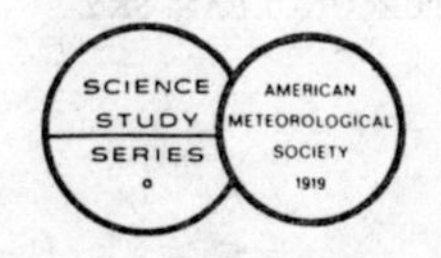

Published by Anchor Books
Doubleday & Company, Inc.
Garden City, New York

The Science Study Series edition is the
first publication of THE UNCLEAN SKY

Library of Congress Catalog Card Number 66–17454

Printed in the United States of America

THE SCIENCE STUDY SERIES

This book is one of a number that will appear in the Science Study Series through the collaboration of Educational Services Incorporated and the American Meteorological Society.

The Science Study Series was begun, in 1959, as a part of the Physical Science Study Committee's program to create a new physics course for American high schools. The Committee started its work in 1956, at the Massachusetts Institute of Technology, but subsequently became the nucleus of Educational Services Incorporated, of Watertown, Massachusetts, which has carried on the development of new curricula in several fields of education, both in the United States and abroad. The work in physics has had financial support from the National Science Foundation, the Ford Foundation, the Fund for the Advancement of Education, and the Alfred P. Sloan Foundation.

The purpose of the Series is to provide up-to-date, understandable, and authoritative reading in science for secondary school students and the lay public. The list of published and projected volumes covers many aspects of science and technology and also includes history and biography.

Selected Topics in the Atmospheric Sciences

The American Meteorological Society, with the objectives of disseminating knowledge of meteorology and advancing professional ideals, has sponsored a number of educational programs designed to stimulate interest in the atmospheric sciences. One such program, supported by the National Science Foundation, involves the development of a series of monographs for secondary school students and laymen, and since the intended audiences and the standards of excellence were similar, arrangements were made to include their volumes on meteorology in the Science Study Series.

This series within a series is guided by a Board of Editors consisting of James M. Austin, Massachusetts Institute of Technology; Richard A. Craig, Florida State University; James G. Edinger, University of California, Los Angeles; and Verne N. Rockcastle, Cornell University. The Society solicits manuscripts on various topics in the atmospheric sciences by distinguished scientists and educators.

PREFACE

Pollution of the air we breathe has been going on for a long time. As population and industry have grown, the quantities of coal and oil consumed have kept pace. The amounts of gaseous and solid contaminants added to the air have increased at a pronounced rate. In recent years there has been growing concern all over the world. Rightly, attention has been directed to the sources of pollutants, but not enough scrutiny has been given to change in the atmosphere itself. One of the primary aims of this book has been to show the relationships between air pollution and the weather.

This small volume does not attempt to give a comprehensive discussion of all sources of air pollution and the biological effects thereof. It has concentrated on the smokes put into the atmosphere by chimneys and the tailpipes of automobiles. Two important sources of air pollution—pesticides and radioactive particles—are barely mentioned. This omission should not be taken as an indication that they are of minor importance. On the contrary. They may, in certain circumstances, pose very serious dangers. They are sufficiently important and have enough unique properties to be worthy of special treatment in another book.

LOUIS J. BATTAN

PREFACE

Pollution of the atmosphere has been going on for a long time. As population and industry have grown, the quantities of coal and oil consumed have kept pace. The amounts of gaseous and solid contaminants added to the air have increased at a pronounced rate. In consequence, there has been growing concern all over the world. Rightly, attention has been directed to the sources of pollutants, but not enough scrutiny has been given to changes in the atmosphere itself. One of the primary aims of this book has been to show the interrelations between air pollution and the weather.

This small volume does not attempt to give a comprehensive discussion of all sources of air pollution and the biological effects thereof. It has concentrated on the smoke put into the atmosphere by chimneys and the tailpipes of automobiles. Two important sources of air pollution—pesticides and radioactive particles—are barely mentioned. This omission should not be taken as an indication that they are of minor importance. On the contrary. They [illegible] special characteristics, pose very serious dangers, are sufficiently important and have enough unique properties to be worthy of special treatment in another book.

L[illegible] J. BATTAN

CONTENTS

THE UNCLEAN SKY

Chapter I

SMOKE IN THE AIR

The third of December 1952 was a delightful winter day in London, England. The weatherman reported that a cold front had passed in the night, and by noon the temperature reached 42°F. The relative humidity was about 70 per cent. The wind blew pleasantly from the north, and the fluffy cumulus clouds for which the English climate in its smiling moments is famous dotted the sky. All in all, it was a beautiful day.

The elderly and the sick, in particular, enjoyed sitting in the sun and drinking in the clear, clean air flowing from the North Sea. It swept across all England, pushing ahead of it the smoke from Midlands factories and city chimney pots. London was just on the southeastern edge of a large anticyclone, that is to say, a region where the atmospheric pressure was high. Around this center of high pressure the winds were blowing clockwise.

On December 4 the anticyclone, following a familiar pattern, had moved southeastward. Its center was a few hundred miles to the west of London. The winds had turned slightly and were coming from the north-northwest, but they were slower than they had been. Several layers of clouds almost obscured the sky. A higher deck of cloud, at about 10,000 feet, could be glimpsed through breaks in the lower expanse of uniform, dark gray stratus clouds. They shut out the sun as well as the sky. At noon the temperature was 38°F, and the relative humidity was a moist 82 per cent.

The smell of smoke was in the air. From thousands of

chimneys the unburnt remains of coal—the gases, the soot, and the specks of ash—floated silently into the atmosphere. Large particles fell to the rooftops, the streets, on hats and coats. The smaller smoke particles drifted with the air. When playing children ran in or out of houses, gusts of air carried the particles and gases indoors. The fumes found a way even into buildings whose doors and windows were closed. As the temperature inside and outside the building changed, the structures "breathed in" polluted air and exhaled cleaner air.

Nevertheless, all factors considered, the weather on December 4 was not too bad—it only seemed so in comparison to the day before. During the days that followed Londoners were to learn how really dreadful the weather could become.

On the fifth, the high pressure center had moved almost over London. The winds were very light. Patches of fog reduced visibility, making it difficult to get about. At noon the air temperature was 33°F and the relative humidity about 80 per cent.

The odor of smoke was becoming stronger. The winds were too weak to carry away the chimney's outpourings of smoke. In the lowest few thousand feet of the atmosphere both smoke and moisture accumulated. People began to complain to their neighbors. Cab drivers muttered about the fog.

The next day conditions had worsened. Dense fog blotted out the sky entirely. The city was under the western end of the anticyclone. At noon the temperature was down to 28°F, and the relative humidity had risen to 100 per cent. Visibility was measured in tens of feet. All airplane flights were canceled, and only the most experienced driver (or the fool) ventured on the road with his automobile. Pedestrians groped their way along the pavements.

The anemometers—that is, the wind speed instruments —yielded a very important measurement. Perhaps it would be correct to say that they failed to yield a measurement. At any rate, the wind reading was a dead calm. The air was not moving fast enough to turn the cups on the apparatus, a wind speed of not more then a mile or two per hour. It was a situation in which a barely perceptible breath would move first one way, then the other.

As the air hung virtually stagnant over the city, the smoking stoves, furnaces, and fireplaces fed it with poison. The fog droplets captured some of the smoke gases and particles. It was not a clean fog any more. No longer tiny droplets of clean water, it was composed of a mixture of smoke and fog, a mixture we call *smog*.

The smog bathed the city in its own debris, attacking all living things. People felt it in their eyes. Tears streaked down faces. Every breath meant a lungful of polluted air. Wherever groups of people congregated, coughing could be heard. At school the lecturers had to raise their voices above the hacking and whooping. At church a clergyman coughed his way through a prayer that conditions might soon improve.

But the weather in London on December 7 and 8 was no better. The smog was terrible. The old and sick, who just a few days earlier had been enjoying what was then a balmy breeze from the north, were suffering badly from the foul air, finding it hard to breathe. Even some of the young were barely enduring; the ones with respiratory diseases found it hard to get oxygen into their lungs. To asthmatics the smog was torture. Patients crowded London hospitals, casualties of the smog. Many did not survive.

On December 9 there was a slight improvement in the weather. The fog was still present, but the wind was blowing slowly and fairly steadily from the south. Some clean air was mixing with the smog and diluting it. At noon the temperature was about 38°F, with a relative humidity of 95 per cent.

The next day a cold front passed over England. Brisk, west winds brought in air from the North Atlantic. Londoners, filling their lungs again with fresh, clean air, heaved a collective sigh of relief. In retrospect the five days seemed a nightmare.

In the period of smog about four thousand people died, directly or indirectly victims of its effects. Most of the dead had been weakened already by age or lung troubles, and the week of pollution had been too great an extra strain. Who knows how long they would have lived had not nature conspired to bring about five consecutive days of heavily polluted air?

In addition to the fatalities there were uncounted thousands whose illnesses were aggravated severely or who developed respiratory ailments for the first time. Finally, among the sufferers there were the families of the sick and dead, the survivors whose lives were changed by their losses. By any standard, certainly, it was a catastrophe, mass homicide by poison, with the weather accessory before the fact.

The great London smog came about because moist, foggy air over the city stagnated while huge quantities of smoke were spewed into it. The atmosphere over London became a dump for the finely divided waste matter that rose from smokestacks and chimneys. The use of coal certainly was an important contributor to the problem, but it was not the sole cause.

Although London has long been celebrated for its fogs, it is by no means unique in having air pollution problems. Virtually every large city in the world has to contend with the effects of smoke particles and gases and other irritating substances. Many smaller towns have to worry on the same score. Towns in river valleys can find themselves in real trouble when winds become light, especially in the autumn and winter.

The citizens of Donora, Pennsylvania, know about smog.

This town, with a population of about twelve thousand, is situated some twenty miles south-southeast of Pittsburgh on the shore of the Monongahela River. Baseball fans might recognize it as the hometown of the great Stan Musial. To atmospheric scientists it is better known for the tragedy of October 1948.

Donora is an industrial town. Smokestacks from steel, zinc, and sulfuric acid plants form the skyline. They have been pouring smoke into the air for a long time. Fortunately for the residents, as for inhabitants of most cities, winds ordinarily mix the pollutants through a fairly deep layer of the atmosphere. Usually the polluted air, carried downwind, spreads out over great distances.

Over the years residents of western Pennsylvania have become accustomed to smoke. But it was not always so. Some old-timers can remember sitting on the back porch and clearly seeing the mountaintops twenty or thirty miles away. This degree of visibility used to be common, but not any more. As the great city of Pittsburgh and its neighbors grew, the factories grew with them, and the air lost its clarity. Smoke from homes and office buildings, from the tailpipes of the ever-increasing number of cars and trucks, all contributed to the loss of transparency. The thin veil in the atmosphere was drawn across the remaining beauty of the countryside.

Of course, the contamination has been doing much worse than degrading the visibility. Each breath of air carries with it thousands and thousands of tiny grains of undesirable matter. Scientists have coined the word *aerosols* to designate these solid or liquid particles in the air. The largest aerosols are captured in the nose or throat. Some of the smaller ones go in and out of the lungs untouched, but others deposit themselves on the linings of the lungs. With the years the coatings become thicker and more widespread. Slowly, secretly, but steadily, the lungs of people exposed to heavily polluted air are being weakened. The foundation for serious disease is being established. This more deadly degradation is happening today all over the world, but particularly in the larger industrial cities.

The slow decline of health frequently goes unobserved. Until too late, who looks inside a lung to see how badly coated it is with tar? But autopsies clearly show the state of lungs after years or decades of exposure to polluted air.

Because the effects are slow and cumulative, a great many people do not seem to take the air pollution problem seriously. Only a sudden massive blow can lift the public chin off its chest, such a blow as was delivered in London and, earlier, in Donora, Pennsylvania.*

As in London four years later, the weather was the

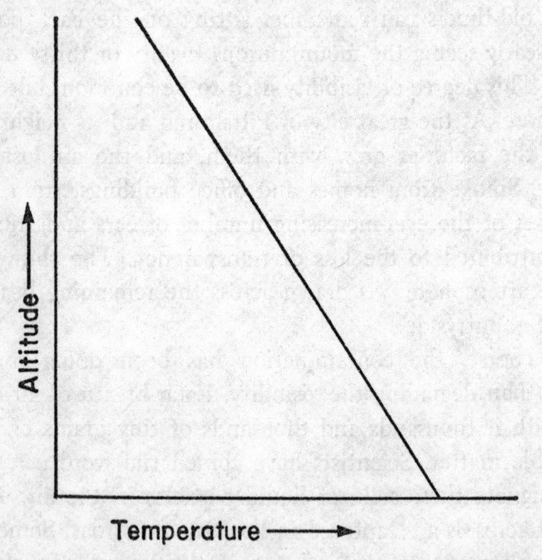

Fig. 1 Normally air temperature decreases with height.

* A discussion of the meteorological factors in this instance has been given by Robert D. Fletcher in *Weatherwise*, June 1949.

wicked conspirator at Donora. A high pressure area moved over western Pennsylvania on October 26, 1948 and remained fairly stationary for the next five days. Winds in the lowest 2000 feet of the atmosphere were quite weak. Mostly they were between a dead calm and 3 m.p.h., but for brief periods they were slightly higher. The air was "thermally stable," a formal description implying that there was very little vertical motion of the air.

Meteorologists have long known that the amount of vertical motion of the atmosphere depends to an important extent on how the temperature varies with altitude. Near the ground air temperature normally decreases with height (see Figure 1). When the rate of decrease is rapid—that is, when it is greater than 5.5°F per 1000 feet—there is a pronounced tendency toward vertical air mixing. On the other hand, when the air temperature increases with

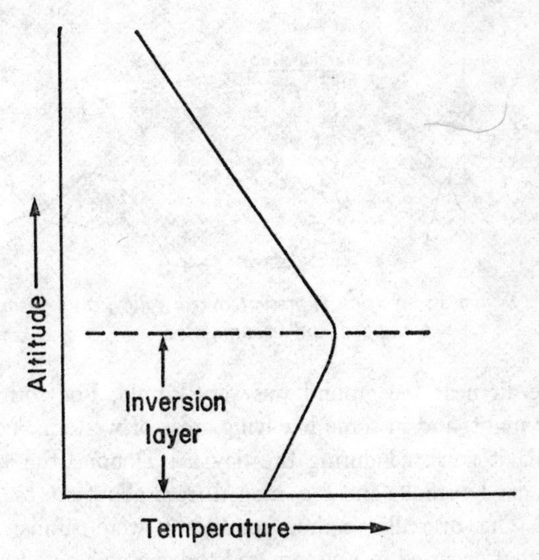

Fig. 2 When temperature increases with height, an inversion is said to exist.

height, vertical air motions are suppressed. This temperature structure is called a "temperature inversion" because it is "inverted" from the normal condition of temperature decreasing with height. (See Figure 2.) The relationship between vertical air movements and temperature changes will be discussed in some detail later. At this point, it is enough to recognize that with a temperature inversion near the ground the air essentially is trapped. Trapped also are the particles and gases polluting it.

Donora, lying near the bottom of a steep valley, is about 500 feet below the surrounding terrain. During the period October 26 to 31, 1948, an inversion capped the valley. Pilot reports and weather balloons showed that the cap, at least part of the time, was less than a thousand feet above the town. Thus, smoke fed to the atmosphere was largely confined within the valley walls and the inversion top. (See Figure 3.)

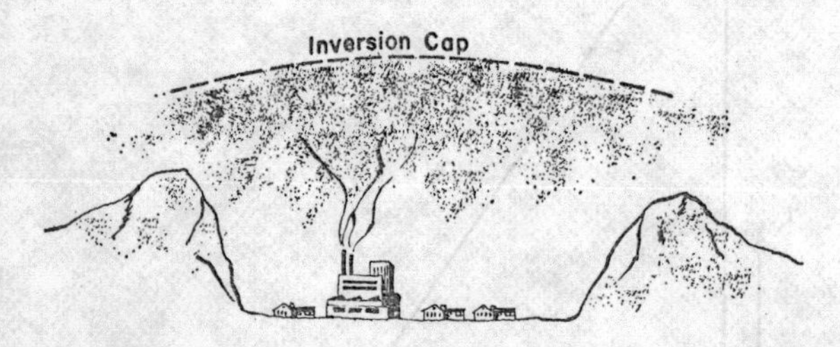

Fig. 3 *When an inversion is present over a valley, smoke can be trapped and accumulated.*

The air near the ground was very humid. Fog formed in the night, and in some low-lying areas of western Pennsylvania it persisted during the day. At Donora, the visibility, cut by smoke and fog, ranged from about 0.6 to 1.5 miles. The over-all weather conditions were similar to those that occurred in London, and the consequences tragically alike.

During the five-day period, air pollution accumulated to such levels that several thousand people became ill. A great many required hospitalization, and twenty died.

There have been other air pollution disasters. A well-known incident happened in December 1930 along the Meuse Valley in Belgium between the towns of Liége and Huy. A prolonged smog trapped under an inversion caused the deaths of sixty-three people. Fortunately, homicide by air pollution on this scale does not occur often, but it is nonetheless fact that the gradual sickening effects are widespread.

Probably the most notorious smog area in the world is Los Angeles, California. There are smokestacks in abundance. In addition, there are automobiles in uncountable profusion. Coupled with these prolific smoke sources are the two natural elements which were so promiment in Donora: namely, temperature inversions and a mountainous topography.

The Los Angeles Basin, on the shore of the Pacific Ocean, is walled by mountains to the east and north. Although out to sea moderately strong surface winds blow, usually from the northwest, they do not cross the shoreline. Near the shore and along the almost east–west coastline, the breezes are westerly or southwesterly, and are weak. These winds carry air over the city toward the mountain blockade.

An important part of the weather pattern of this area is a persistent anticyclone. It is part of the more or less permanent band of high pressure which belts the earth at about latitude 30°. Los Angeles is at the eastern end of one area of high pressure called the Pacific Anticyclone. The air in this area commonly is sinking. As will be shown later, the effect of this sinking is to cause the air to become warmer. Since the subsiding air usually does not descend all the way to the ground, the sinking leads to the formation of a temperature inversion at an altitude of about 2000 feet.

There is still another factor contributing to the formation of this inversion. Flowing toward the south and east along the California coast is an ocean current named (quite sensibly) the California Current. During the spring and early summer this water is relatively cold. Warmer air from over the Pacific Ocean is cooled as it moves over the cold ocean water on its passage across the coast toward the Los Angeles area. The cooling of the air near the ground and the warming of the air aloft because of the sinking motion lead to the formation of strong and persistent temperature inversions over Los Angeles. They act as caps to trap surface air and to prevent the rising of pollutants to higher altitudes where they might pass over the mountains.

As the smoke pours out of the stacks and exhaust pipes, the concentrations can reach those levels where they cause great distress. Unlike the London smogs, which are a mixture of heavy fog with smoke, the Los Angeles smogs usually are not associated with dense fog. It is more nearly a haze than a fog. There is not sufficient moisture in the air to produce a great many water droplets. It is the billions and billions of mostly solid particles in the air that obscure visibility. Sometimes they get slightly wet. They reduce visibility, but not to the extent of a dense fog.

Nevertheless, even though the visibility is good enough to drive a car safely, the Los Angeles smog sometimes causes such severe eye irritation that driving becomes hazardous. The chemical substances from unburned gasoline and other fuels, if they are sufficiently concentrated, can set the tear ducts flowing. The smog also makes life difficult for people with respiratory problems. Certain types of plant life suffer even more than people do from the polluted air.

In a later chapter, we shall consider the specific substances and gases which have been added to the atmosphere in the form of gases and aerosols, but at this point it is enough to know that when concentrations of normally painless smokes become large enough they can be toxic. Fortunately, the Los Angeles smogs have not reached the levels of toxicity that caused the London and Donora disasters, but it is commonplace to have sufficient pollution to bother a large fraction of the population.

In 1947 the people of Los Angeles formed an Air Pollution Control District to study the nature of pollutants and their sources, and to see what might be done to improve the situation. Almost twenty years and many millions of dollars later, Los Angeles still has a major air pollution problem. But the city officials have learned a great deal about their local problem and have taken some positive steps toward solution.

In a later section we shall return to air pollution in cities and towns, but now let us look at other sources of smoke in the atmosphere. One of them has been with us throughout geological time.

Volcanoes

Volcanoes sometimes hurl tremendous quantities of smoke and debris into the atmosphere. It has been estimated that a single strong eruption can throw up 100 billion cubic yards of fine particles. These substances and condensed gases may rise more than 70,000 feet, into the stratosphere. The smaller bits may take several years to return to earth.

Except in the close vicinity of an eruption the outpourings from volcanoes do not present a threat to human lungs or plant life. But the tiny particles thrown up to reside in the upper levels of the atmosphere do influence the lives of us all. A variety of atmospheric processes may be involved.

It has been found that an explosive volcano such as the eruption of Krakatoa, in Java, in 1883, can inject so many particles that they seriously interfere with the amount of solar energy reaching the earth. In the Krakatoa eruption the grains were estimated to have an average diameter of only about 0.002 millimeters (about 0.00008 inch), but there were enough to affect significantly the incoming rays of the sun. The particles were too small to reflect the outgoing heat waves from the earth. The net effect was to cause a small but important change in the heat budget of the earth. It took several years for all the particles to fall out of the upper atmosphere. During this period they were carried around the earth by the winds and spread out to form a blanket over the globe.

The over-all effect was to cause a general cooling. Fortunately, the particles did eventually fall out. If they had not, temperatures on the earth would have fallen, slowly but steadily, to the point possibly where a new ice age might have been started.

Volcanic dust in the high atmosphere does produce some pleasant effects. Less solar energy reaches the earth through the cloud of minute pieces of solid matter because the particles scatter the sunlight. You might have thought that they would mostly absorb it, but this has been found not to be the case. The particles scatter the sun's light, but not all the colors are scattered equally. Some are affected more than others. The longer wave lengths of light, the ones at the red end of the color spectrum, are scattered less than those at the violet end. As a result, the various colors of sunlight are separated out. This process becomes particularly apparent at sunrise or sunset, when the sun's rays have a long distance to travel horizontally through the atmosphere to reach our eyes. With clear skies or, at most, only a few clouds you see brilliantly colored skies with deep hues of blue and lavender. These colors are scattered downwards by the dust while the reds pass through the atmosphere with little scattering.

Forest Fires

Another natural means of air pollution is the smoke from forest fires. Every year there are many thousands of forest and brush fires. A high percentage are started by careless people; a great many more are started by lightning. According to records of the United States Forest Service, over the period 1954 to 1963 in the United States some 1,200,000 fires burned nearly 6,000,000 acres of forests.

The local effects of smoke pollution can be quite serious. A fire may go on for several weeks. During its lifetime areas downwind may be shrouded in a dense smoke that makes it hard to breathe. Sometimes the population must be moved out. The problems raised by forest fires are clear. Some of the solutions are also obvious. Campaigns of public education about fire safety of the kind conducted by the Forest Service are vital. Smokey the Bear has earned, many times over, his prominent place in society.

There will continue to be need for research on artificial means of lightning suppression and better techniques for fire fighting. Fortunately, the smoke usually does not constitute a major source of atmospheric pollution except in the vicinity of the fire.

Chapter II

SOILS, SALTS, AND COSMIC DUSTS

While it is true that fires in stoves, furnaces, engines, forests, or deep in the earth are major sources of air pollution, they are not the only ones. They most certainly contribute fantastic numbers of toxic and destructive particles to the atmosphere, but, fortunately, the atmosphere is very large and can hold almost unbelievable quantities of solid and gaseous material.

Consider for a minute the mass of the atmosphere. We know that the average sea level pressure is about 14.7 pounds per square inch. The total surface area of the earth is about 8×10^{17}*, or 800,000,000,000,000,000, square inches. The total weight of the atmosphere is the pressure multiplied by the area. This product yields a value of 118 $\times 10^{17}$ pounds, or about 6×10^{15} tons, of air. In such an enormous quantity of air smoke and dust particles easily can get lost. Millions of tons of particles can float around in a finely dispersed form and never be noticed. For example, six million tons of pollutants would amount to only about one ton of particles for a billion tons of air if they were distributed uniformly. Unfortunately, the pollutants are not uniformly mixed through the entire atmosphere. As is the case with so many natural phenomena, rain for example, some places have values much greater than average, other places much smaller than average.

* In science large numbers are expressed in orders of magnitude; that is, in powers of ten. The term 8×10^{17} means 8 multiplied seventeen times by ten.

We know from observation that there usually are vast numbers of tiny solid and liquid particles in the air, and a great many people live long lives without knowing or caring about them—providing, that is, the concentrations of particles are small. But when the *concentrations* get excessively large, when the mass of pollutants is large with respect to the mass of air, then we begin to have troubles. We don't even notice pollutants present in parts per billion, but when they occur in parts per million, our bodies protest. Large numbers of aerosols composed of particular types of chemical substances not only irritate, but do bodily harm and sometimes can kill. Certain gases contaminating the air are no less lethal.

The total mass of solid pollutants in the atmosphere is estimated to be about 10 million tons. The different kinds of smoke we discussed in Chapter I constitute part of this total. Other particles in the air come from the surface of the earth, from the oceans, and a small amount from outer space. Human activities sometimes pollute the air on purpose. For example, the spraying of insecticides adds many poisons to the atmosphere.

Soil Particles

Most solid particles tend to stick together or to other solid objects. The amount of sticking depends, of course, on the substance.

Consider any finely divided substance and see how it behaves. Stick your finger in something as powdery as baking flour, for example. When you pull your finger out, a great deal of the flour falls off. You can easily blow off most of the rest. But not all. A thin layer adheres tightly and will not yield even when you blow as hard as you can.

You may have noticed that cool walls in a building get dirtier than warm ones do. The explanation is that more tiny particles come into contact with the cool surfaces. Air molecules are in constant motion in all directions. The warm air near a warm wall is made up of molecules moving at speeds higher than those of the molecules of cooler air near a cooler wall. Bombardment of minute aerosols by the faster air molecules drives them toward the cool wall until they finally hit it and stick. Blowing will not get them off. You have to rub or wash them off. The fact that small particles adhere firmly to one another has important consequences.

Have you ever been on a desert? If so, the good visibility probably impressed you. If there were mountains around, you probably could see them at distances of thirty or forty miles or more. In more humid areas visibilities of ten to twenty miles are generally considered to represent good seeing. In large industrialized cities the visibility is still worse.

Why is air so transparent in the deserts? One important reason probably occurs to you at once—the low moisture content of the air. The small quantities of water vapor in the air allow light to pass through the atmosphere with little absorption. For this reason, the skies at night are magnificent. Even without a telescope you often can see stars which in more humid regions usually are obscured. That is not to say that in the central United States, for instance, astronomical conditions always are inferior to those over the desert regions of the Southwest. In wintertime, when a very cold, dry mass of air from the Arctic sweeps through Madison, Wisconsin, say, the view of the stars is outstanding. In the deserts this degree of visibility is common. For this reason there are many astronomical observatories in the arid regions of the world.

The visibility normally is quite good in the deserts for reasons other than the deficiency of water vapor alone. A second reason is the small numbers of aerosols in the atmosphere. Part of the explanation is that there are few smoke-producing industries. Such manufacturing processes as steel making or oil refining require large quantities of water. Since deserts are by definition regions short of water, many industries cannot operate there.

One should not be led to believe, however, that there are no smoke-producing industries at all. Copper refineries, for example, sometimes may produce sufficient smoke to mar the view of colorful mountain panoramas. Power-generating plants using oil or gas contribute to the pall which cuts the view to "only forty miles," as veteran desert dwellers sometimes put it. Some decades ago in southern Arizona it was common to be able to see more than eighty miles.

There is still another reason why desert air is so clear. It has to do with compactness of the soil and the size and adhesion of the soil particles. Unless the ground has been torn up for construction purposes, a road or a building, or for farming the ground in the desert is solid and compact. Even with sparse vegetation, with cactus, mesquite, creosote bush, and so forth, the earth is held firmly together. Persons who study soil call it "desert pavement."

Light winds do no more than cause the bushes to wave gently back and forth. In order to lift soil particles from the undisturbed desert floor, strong winds are needed. It has been estimated that in the Santa Cruz Valley, in Arizona, winds of greater than 30 to 40 m.p.h. are required to pick up and scatter soil particles. In this area the desert is spotted with vegetation supported by an average rainfall of about 10 inches per year.

In the very arid regions, where rainfall is below 2 or 3 inches per year, you find the kinds of deserts that make the romantic backgrounds for movies of Lawrence of Arabia and the Foreign Legion. Such a desert is the one in California just west of Yuma, the Colorado Desert, where there is no vegetation, only sand. Even light breezes in this region cause the fine grains to blow.

In the deserts made up of very fine sand with particle

diameters of about 0.1 millimeter (about 0.004 inch), moderate to strong winds can lift minute sand particles to great altitudes, especially on days when the atmosphere is unstable. The blowing of soil occurs in any other region where the ground is dry and loosened by digging or plowing. When there is little vegetation with roots to bind the soil and little moisture to cement together the grains of soil, even moderate winds can cause the particles to rise to altitudes of over two miles.

The manner in which wind excavates the soil is interesting. When the wind moves over broken soil, it pushes against individual grains and dislodges them from their neighbors and starts them rolling over the ground. Particles as large as 1 millimeter (about 0.04 inch) in diameter require very strong winds before they start to move. Usually smaller ones go first. Those with diameters of about 0.2 millimeter (about 0.008 inch) begin moving with winds of about 10 to 15 m.p.h. They roll and slide over the ground.

Particles with diameters of only about 0.1 millimeter roll faster than the larger ones. After traveling a short distance, they may strike another protruding particle and suddenly shoot upward. This is called *saltation,* from the jumping movement of the particles. The height of the leap depends on such properties as the size and weight of the particle, the roughness of the ground, and the speed of the wind. Some particles jump less than an inch; others go as high as several feet. While in the air some of the grains spin at speeds as high as 1000 revolutions per second.

When a particle is airborne, the wind pushes it forward more rapidly. Arching earthward, it continues to accelerate until it strikes the ground. Sometimes it rebounds again and repeats the jumping routine. (See Figure 4.) On impact with the surface the particle loses some energy, and the second jump is smaller than the first. Some energy is lost in knocking other particles into the air. Other soil

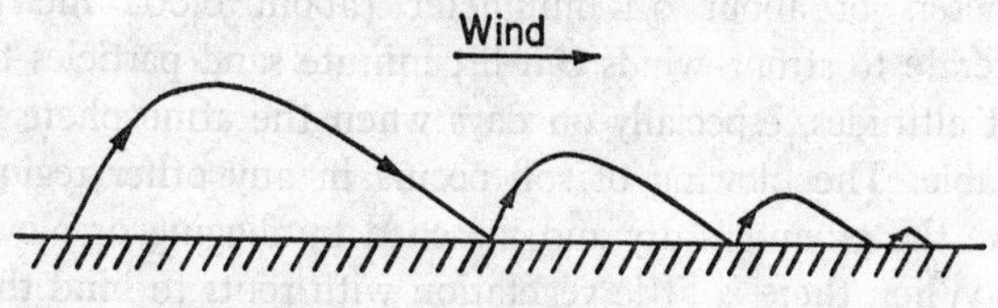

Fig. 4 The trajectory of a soil particle during saltation.

grains having masses too great for them to leap into the air are started in motion over the surface. Once started, they continue moving under the force of the wind.

Some soil grains are very fine dust with diameters of only 0.001 millimeter (about 0.00004 inch). The winds normally cannot dislodge them from the soil, but blasting by larger particles in saltation can kick the minute grains free. Once they get into the air they may be carried in rising currents of air to altitudes of two or three miles. They fall so slowly with respect to still air that they may remain in the atmosphere for many weeks. Usually they stay until rain or snow particles wash them back to the ground.

In summary, it should be noted that the effect of wind erosion depends on the strength of the winds and on the structure of the soils, particularly the size of the grains. On sands with particle diameters greater than 1 millimeter winds have little effect because the grains are too heavy to be moved. When the soils are composed of very small grains, diameters less than 0.05 millimeter, wind alone cannot separate the particles held together by strong forces. The soils with particle diameters of about 0.1 millimeter are most easily eroded. In mixed soils these grains leap into the air and on crashing back to earth break loose the bonds that bind the fine dusts and blast them into the air. These are the ones which remain aloft to add to the pollution of the atmosphere.

Thus we see that for fine dust to get into the air, it is

necessary that some impaction forces be exerted on the soil. Larger grains bouncing across a field can do it. Vehicles can do it. One trip down an unpaved country road behind a car or truck makes it dramatically clear how four spinning tires can throw up clouds of dust.

Animals also can stir up large quantities of fine soil particles. Western movies with stampedes of cattle or horses illustrate in a convincing manner how the pounding of hoofs on bare soil can create billowing clouds of powdery soil.

Air Bubbles in the Sea

The crashing of waves on a rocky shore is the sound of music for millions of people. The waves rolling in from great distances seem like messengers from romantic places far away. These sights and sounds are universal. They are the same in Scotland as in California, in Italy as in Texas. As the water beats on a stony shore or comes tumbling over a sandy beach, it stirs up white streaks of foam. Sea water is sprayed into the air; air is stirred into the sea. Before the next wave comes running in most of the spray falls back to the ocean and most of the air rises back to the atmosphere. But not all.

If you had extra-powerful eyes to examine the air of a foamy surf, you would see that some of the smallest water droplets remain in the air. Indeed, some of them move to great altitudes on currents of rising air.

The naked eye cannot see the minute water droplets, but there is some easily detected indirect evidence for their presence. Examine the chrome-covered bumpers of automobiles which have been near the seashore for an extended period of time. You will see bad pitting. By contrast, the deterioration of the shiny metal on cars operated in warm regions far from the oceans is quite minor. Of course, you find that vehicles in snowy areas are in about the same condition as those by the sea and for the same general reason—the action of salt on the roads. In a northern city, say Chicago, salt is spread over the streets in abundant quantities during snowy winters. A car cannot escape being splashed with water containing large quantities of salt. The brine seeps through the pores of the chrome and corrodes the metal.

Along a seashore the air commonly contains tremendous quantities of minute droplets of sea water. They are more or less suspended and carried by the winds. The larger ones fall toward the surface. The smallest are transported horizontally and may be lifted to altitudes of many thousands of feet. Near the coast, this cloud of sea water droplets can have important effects on all objects which are not salt resistant. The larger droplets settle on such objects as automobiles and, as we mentioned, do their dirty work on the chrome and paint. They also can corrode other metal surfaces. When weather conditions are just right, the sea particles can grow by condensation and lead to fog formation. Falling fog droplets can coat the landscape with a wet film. When the film dries, a thin layer of salt is left behind.

What happens to sea salt droplets that do not fall quickly back to their place of origin? Of course, no one can tell exactly what will be the history of each droplet, but we have a pretty good idea what happens to most of them.

As droplets move away from the water surface they come under the influence of drier air, either by ascending to higher altitudes or by going farther inland. In the dry air the water begins to evaporate. If the air is dry enough, virtually all the water can evaporate, leaving only a tiny particle of sea salt. Among atmospheric scientists concerned with aerosols, it is common to hear this term, "sea salt." It refers to all the salts in the sea. There are many of them, but by far the largest quantity is in the form of *sodium chloride* or ordinary table salt. Another important salt is magnesium chloride. It is present in small amounts, but it has a great affinity for water. By this expression we mean that water begins to condense on magnesium chloride when the relative humidity is quite low, about 60 per cent. When table salt has not been refined completely and has a little bit of magnesium chloride mixed in, its effects are disturbingly obvious on a humid day. Even on days that are not excessively humid, water molecules from the air condense on the salt crystals. They stick together as if held by glue, and nothing comes through the holes in the salt shaker.

As you would expect, the size and numbers of salt particles in the atmosphere depend on geographical location. In regions of heavy surf with breaking waves the number of particles is high. It depends on the wind velocity; the stronger the winds the more the rolling and splashing of waves, and the more sea salt thrown into the atmosphere. At increasing altitudes and distances from the ocean there is a general decrease in both the size and number of particles.

Sea salt aerosols are important in cloud and rain formation. Water condensing on them forms cloud droplets. The largest droplets can grow by colliding with smaller ones and reach the ground as rain. Because of the way salt particles act, we call them *condensation nuclei.* They are not the only condensation nuclei in the atmosphere, but they appear to be the source for most of the larger cloud droplets.

Let us examine some pertinent numbers. Near the ocean, salt particles in the lowest few thousands of feet of the atmosphere range in diameter from below 0.0001 millimeter to about 0.01 millimeter. The smallest ones are found in concentrations of several hundred per cubic centimeter. The largest ones, often called *giant condensation nuclei,* are found to be present in numbers of several hundred per cubic meter. Because of their original large size and the fact that in a rising moist air they become large cloud droplets as water condenses on them, giant nuclei fall out of the atmosphere fairly rapidly. On the other hand, the very tiny particles, those smaller than 0.001 millimeter, may stay in the air for many weeks. In the course of their residence in the atmosphere they may travel for even greater distances than the waves which died a foamy death bringing them into existence.

The precise method in which sea salt aerosols are produced is somewhat surprising. When a rushing wall of water pounds into a breakwater, throwing a spray into the air, a large quantity of salt water obviously has been flung into the atmosphere. Some of the droplets produced in this way are small enough to remain in the air as aerosols, but most of them are so large that they fall back into the sea.

The chief mechanism by which most salt nuclei are produced operates on the bubbles of air that are mixed into the water as the waves break. The bubbles rush back toward the surface just as an inflated inner tube released under water would. Just before the bubble breaks through the surface, it is coated with a thin film of water. This very fine skin of water bursts suddenly, and water fragments are thrown into the air. The fragments form water droplets perhaps 0.001 millimeter in diameter.

At the instant of collapse of the film of water there is still a "crater" in the water, the volume occupied by the air bubble. Water rushes in from all sides to fill in the void. The air in the crater, forced upward, blows the tiny droplets away from the sea surface. The collapsing crater also leads to the formation of a small jet of water up the center of the crater. The jet breaks up and produces one to five fairly large drops which are projected upward at surprisingly high velocities, about 175 m.p.h. according to Duncan Blanchard of the Woods Hole Oceanographic Institution. These drops, usually greater than about 0.01 millimeter in diameter, fall back to the surface quickly. The air bubbles producing most of the sea salt nuclei are about 3 millimeters in diameter, still small but easily visible by eye. Each bubble can manufacture from 100 to 200 tiny droplets to feed the atmospheric supply of aerosols.

Most of the air bubbles in the sea get there because of turbulent action of the water, the breaking of waves or splashing against steep coast lines. However, this is not the only way to produce bubbles. In recent years, it has been recognized that volcanic eruptions near the sea can cause boiling and bubbling of ocean water like the churnings of some monstrous witch's cauldron. Hot lava flowing into the sea is the fire under the pot. The breaking of bubbles of steam causes tremendous numbers of sea particles to be injected into the atmosphere.

There is no question that in the vicinity of lava flow the concentration of nuclei can be very great, but there are few volcanic eruptions into the oceans. The area of the sea so affected is extremely small in comparison to the area over which the waves so commonly break. Thus it is concluded that the dramatic production of bubbles by volcanic violence is secondary in comparison to the steady and widespread supply from turbulent waters.

Cosmic Dust

As the earth moves in its orbit, at a speed of about 19 miles per second, it passes, at regular intervals, through huge clouds of solid particles. They range in size from tiny ones seen only with the most powerful microscope to large ones weighing hundreds of tons. There are many of the small ones but very few of the large ones. In passing through the space dust, the earth's atmosphere "sweeps" out a large number of the particles. The minute ones, with diameters below about 0.002 millimeter, can move through the air toward the ground without being seen. Slightly larger particles melt. But the larger ones, those greater than about 0.1 millimeter, enter the atmosphere in a blaze of light. You probably have seen them streaking across the night sky. They are commonly called "shooting stars." Atmospheric scientists call them *meteoroids*. When they survive the trip through the atmosphere and reach the earth they are called *meteorites*.

Meteoroids are constantly entering the earth's envelope. At night the larger ones can be seen by the light they emit. In daytime the bright background of the sky makes it difficult to see them, but we know they are there. They can be detected by means of radar or with special radio equipment. The numbers of these particles impinging on the envelope increase when the earth is passing through the clouds of cosmic dust.

The greatest of known meteorites struck the earth in Arizona. Imagine what a fantastic sight it must have been when a flaming ball of fire came shooting out of the sky! The original mass was perhaps a million tons. When it struck it must have caused tremors to travel around the globe. On impact it threw millions of tons of rock and soil in all directions and produced the famous Meteor Crater, a hole about a mile in diameter and 600 feet deep. Fortunately, the arrivals of such massive collections of iron and stone from outer space are extremely rare. After all, there is only one Meteor Crater. There are reports of a similar crater in Asia. But the occurrence of two such events over the last several million years is reassuring, statistically: we need not worry about any repetitions.

However, there are tremendous numbers of small particles in the envelope. It has been estimated that over the earth one to two hundred million visible meteors occur every day. You may wonder why a falling meteoroid glows. Intense heat is generated as the meteoroid passes through the atmosphere and is bombarded by air molecules. In outer space the number of gas molecules is so small that we may use the expression "free space." There, particles of matter (including artificial satellites) can move at tremendous speeds and not be heated by what we sometimes refer to as "air friction." But when a solid object descends into the earth's atmosphere it rapidly penetrates regions of high molecular concentrations. At tremendous speeds it is battered by vast numbers of air molecules. The object quickly heats to very high temperature. The process is similar in some respects to the warming of a metal plate hit repeatedly with a hammer. In the case of a meteoroid the effects are multiplied manyfold because of the high speeds involved, about 60,000 m.p.h. When space capsules are brought back to earth, special shields are needed, as you know, to protect the capsule and the astronauts. The shields are heated literally to the burning point. In the case of meteoroids, the particles become white hot and burn up in the brief but fiery descent through the atmosphere.

As already mentioned, the very small particles can pass through the air without being burned. Slowed down by air molecules, they gradually sink toward the earth, taking perhaps thirty days for the trip. It has been estimated that the number of such small particles, called *micrometeorites,* reaching the earth may be as high as 10^{18} particles per day. They represent an influx of about 1000 tons of matter per year. This may seem to be a large quantity of material, but when you spread it over the entire earth it is negligibly thin. However, it does represent one more source of particles in the atmosphere. Although its contribution to pollution is of trivial consequence, it represents a most interesting one.

Plants

Before leaving the subject of sources of aerosols, we should mention one which has not received much attention. Growing plants give off certain volatile, organic substances in the form of gases. They sometimes condense to form liquid aerosols. It has been suspected that they also are adsorbed on the surfaces of other particles in the air. The hazes sometimes seen hovering over forests have been ascribed to vegetative emanations. So far, little is known about their properties or even about their importance in the overall air pollution picture. Additional research is needed.

Chapter III

THE BIGGER THEY ARE, THE HARDER THEY FALL

The particles in the atmosphere range in size from giant meteors to those so tiny that they cannot be seen. The former are extremely rare, so rare in fact that we will not consider them further. The range of diameters of the common aerosols extends from the submicroscopic to perhaps an inch or two. The largest are found in clouds, rain, snow, and, ultimately, hail. All these things are classified as *hydrometeors;* that is, they are atmospheric particles that come about as a result of condensation of water (*hydro*).

Hydrometeors

In subsequent sections we shall be concerned with even smaller things than typical cloud droplets. Before going on, however, let us take a quick glance at some of the properties of some common hydrometeors. Several characteristics are particularly important: diameter, mass, shape, composition, and fall velocity. These quantities are not independent of one another. If you know diameter and composition of a spherical particle, you can calculate the mass and fall velocity.

When discussing the dimensions of small things, you run into inconvenient numbers if English units are employed. The conventional units of length, feet, and yards present no problem when you are talking about the size of a baseball field, the length of a bridge, or the height of a building. Inches are reasonable units when measuring a basketball or a pizza. But when you talk about a cloud droplet, fractions of an inch become quite clumsy.

Most scientists have realized the disadvantage of English units for a great many years and have been in favor of converting all length measurements from the English to the metric system. The value of the latter is particularly evident when very small lengths are involved. As a matter of fact, in most sciences the metric system has been in general use for a long time. We have used it already in the preceding chapter and will use metric units whenever they are convenient. Let us review for any readers not familiar with it. The standard unit of length in the metric system is the meter and

1 meter = 3.28 feet = 1.093 yards.

Of course, if you follow track and field sports, this is not new to you. One of the most popular track events is the 100-yard dash, but this race is run only in English-speaking countries. In most others, and certainly in the Olympics, there is no such event. In its place is the 100-meter dash. It is 109.3 yards long and takes about one more second than the 100-yard dash.

One of the chief inconveniences of English length units is the lack of a standard conversion factor from inches to feet to yards to miles. As we all know, the factors are 12, 3, and 1760, respectively. Another problem is the absence of a generally familiar unit smaller than the inch. This lack becomes annoying when you measure the diameter of a typical cloud droplet and find it to be 0.0004 inch.

In the metric system there are many units smaller than the meter and the conversion factors are all multiples of ten. The common units are the following:

1 meter = 100 centimeters (cm)
1 meter = 1,000 millimeters (mm)
1 meter = 1,000,000 microns

or, expressed in another way:

1 centimeter = 1/100 meter
1 millimeter = 1/1000 meter
1 micron = 1/1,000,000 meter

The diameter of the cloud droplet of 0.0004 inch, which we mentioned earlier, can easily be shown to equal 10 microns. The diameters of cloud droplets are measured in microns, of raindrops in millimeters, and of hail in centimeters.

Figure 5 shows some actual measurements of the numbers of cloud droplets, expressed in numbers per cubic centimeter. It should be recognized that cloud droplets are very nearly spheres of water. Raindrops also resemble spheres of water but are not exactly spheres. Their bottoms are usually flattened. They look more like a hamburger

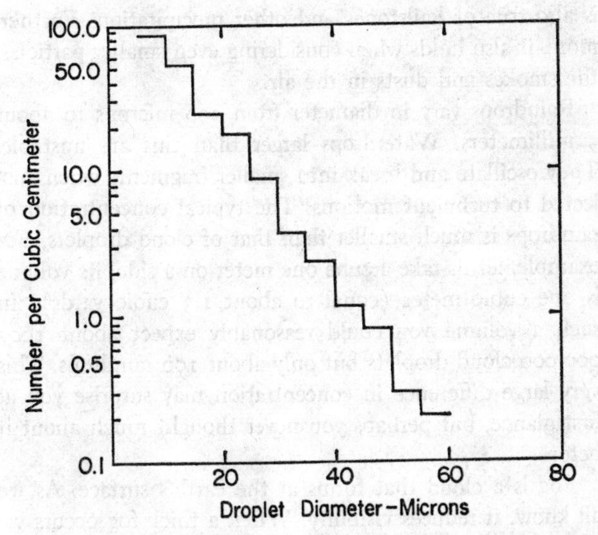

Fig. 5 The concentration of cloud droplets decreases as their sizes increase.

roll than a baseball and, when falling through the air, certainly do not have a teardrop shape.

You may wonder how one discriminates between a raindrop and a cloud droplet. Actually, it is somewhat arbitrary. We say that a waterdrop is a raindrop when its diameter exceeds about 200 microns. Much smaller drops fall slowly, evaporate rapidly, and seldom reach the ground. Much larger drops fall rapidly and evaporate slowly and usually do reach the ground.

Note that in Figure 5 the vertical scale changes as the numbers get larger; the spacing between equal values becomes smaller as you go up the ordinate scale. (For those who want to be specific, this is known as a logarithmic scale.)

Several points on the illustration are worth noting. In general, the larger the particles, the fewer there are. This observation applies also to raindrops. Most of the time it is also true of hailstones and other precipitation. Furthermore, it also holds when considering even smaller particles, the smokes and dusts in the air.

Raindrops vary in diameter from 200 microns to about 5 millimeters. Waterdrops larger than this are unstable. They oscillate and break into smaller fragments when subjected to turbulent motions. The typical concentration of raindrops is much smaller than that of cloud droplets. For example, let us take a cube one meter on a side; its volume is one cubic meter (equal to about 1.3 cubic yards). In such a volume you could reasonably expect about 100,000,000 cloud droplets but only about 100 raindrops. This very large difference in concentration may surprise you at first glance, but perhaps you never thought much about it before.

Fog is a cloud that forms at the earth's surface. As we all know, it reduces visibility. When a thick fog occurs we sometimes cannot recognize objects 10 meters away. The same thing happens when an airplane flies through a thick cloud. The wingtips are sometimes obscured by the billions of intervening cloud droplets. Rain, on the other hand, unless it is very intense, restricts visibility much less than fog does. Occasionally, rain falling through fog will sweep out the smaller droplets and reduce their concentration and lead to improved visibility.

The Fall Speed of Particles

A very important fact about particles in the air is that the speeds of fall depend on the sizes, shapes, and compositions of the particles. The speeds also depend on the properties of the air through which the particles are descending. In considering those factors governing the fall speed, it is best to start off by assuming that the air is perfectly stationary and examine how fast a falling particle approaches the ground. When the air is moving up or down the problems become more complicated.

You may recall from high school physics that any dropped object falls to earth under the influence of gravity. You may also remember that as a result of the pull of gravity *alone*, any object accelerates downward at a constant rate of 32 ft/sec (32 feet per second) for each second elapsed. On this basis, it is easy to calculate the speed of any falling object. For example, a stone dropped over a cliff will be moving at 32 ft/sec after the first second and 64 ft/sec after two seconds of fall, and so forth.

If gravity were the only force at work, the rate at which an object falls would be the same regardless of the size or mass of the object, whether a ping-pong ball or an anvil. This point is easily shown by Newton's famous Second Law of Motion, which usually is written

$$F = M \times a$$

Force = (mass of object) × (acceleration of object)

In our problem the downward force is given simply by

the weight of the object. It is equal to the mass of the object multiplied by the acceleration of gravity (usually denoted by the letter g). Thus we can write,

$$M \times g = M \times a$$

If we divide both sides by M, we are left with

$$a = g$$

Since at the earth's surface g = 32 ft/sec/sec, the acceleration of the object also is equal to 32 ft/sec/sec regardless of its mass or any other property.

Perhaps this is an appropriate place for a few words about the term *mass*, since it has already been used a number of times. When we put any object on a scale and weigh it, we get its *weight*. By definition the mass of the object is its weight divided by the acceleration due to gravity. The mass of the object is the *quantity of matter* and is independent of gravity. A substance having a mass equal to M will have the same mass regardless of where it is, whether on the surface of the earth, at an altitude of 2000 miles (where the acceleration of gravity is of the order of half what it is on the earth's surface) or even on the moon (whose gravitational acceleration is about one-sixth that of the earth). Any object of mass M has the weight $(M \times g)$ on earth, but on the moon its weight would be $(M \times \frac{g}{6})$, that is, one-sixth of the value on the earth.

The mass of any substance is determined by the number of molecules it contains and the structure of the molecules. Consider a cubic centimeter (cm^3) of various substances and their mass. Pure water would represent a mass of about 1.0 gram (a measure of mass in the metric system). A cubic centimeter of ice has a mass of about 0.9 gram; it is less than the mass of water, and hence ice floats. A cubic centimeter of lead is 11 grams, and it sinks rapidly in water. Note that here we are talking about the mass of a single cubic centimeter of matter. This property of matter—namely, the mass in a unit volume—is called the *density*. Thus, water has a density of 1.0 gram/cm^3, ice of 0.9 gram/cm^3, and lead of 11 grams/cm^3.

When we know the volume of any substance (V) and its density (D), the total mass (M) is easily calculated because

$$M = V \times D$$

If water fills a flask with a volume of 10 cm^3, its total mass is equal to 10 grams.

As we have noted, the gram is the metric unit of mass; the English unit is the pound. It is also common to use subdivisions of the gram in powers of ten in the same way as was done with the meter. For example,

1 gram = 1,000 milligrams
1 gram = 1,000,000 micrograms.

When a French housewife goes to the butcher shop and orders meat, she does not ask for a pound of liver, for example. She orders half a kilogram because

1 kilogram = 1,000 grams = 2.2 pounds

Half a kilogram is just a little more than a pound.

With this background, let us return to the particle falling through air. It is important to recognize that, in the earlier discussion of its acceleration (equal to the acceleration of gravity) we neglected to take into account the retarding effect of the air. We assumed, in effect, that our particle would be falling in free space. But, tenuous as it is, air is not free space. Air is made up of a mixture of gases—mostly nitrogen and oxygen. Any object falling through the atmosphere must pass through the field of gas molecules. Although each one is very tiny, the molecules are present in such enormous numbers and move at such speeds that they can be considered to constitute a fluid.

This fluid exerts an upward force upon a falling body, acting to slow down the object. The result is equivalent to a frictional force which slows down an object sliding across a floor. The air is said to exert a *drag force* on a falling particle.

The drag force depends on the properties of the particles as well as on the medium through which they descend. A BB falls faster through air than it does through water, and it moves even slower through oil. If you were to place a BB on the top of an open barrel of tar in summer and had the patience to wait, you would find that the metal sphere would sink ever so slowly through the tar. The speed would depend, of course, on the temperature of the tar. In winter's low temperatures the tar would become hard and brittle, and the BB might not sink at all. If the temperature of the tar were increased, it would become more fluid, its viscosity would decrease, and the BB would start to sink.

In general, the fall speed of any object in any medium depends on the properties of both object and medium. In the case of water spheres falling through air, the essential factors to be considered are the radius of the sphere, the density, and the viscosity of the air. The problem of calculating the fall speeds is not a simple one because the drag force also depends on the speed at which the drop is moving.

Imagine that a particle is dropped into the air. "Pulled" downward by gravity, it starts to accelerate. As soon as the particle begins to move, the air exerts an upward "drag" force. At first the gravitational force is greater than the drag force and the particle continues accelerating, but as it speeds up the drag force increases. After a short time the downward gravitational force is just balanced by the upward drag force. The particle is neither accelerated nor decelerated, and it moves at a constant speed called the *terminal speed.*

The following table gives the terminal speeds of particles of various sizes at sea level.

DROP DIAMETER		APPROXIMATE TERMINAL SPEED		SOURCE
microns	inch (approx)	centimeters/sec	feet/sec (approx)	
1 = 0.0001 cm	0.00004	0.003	0.0001	Smoke, dust
10 = 0.001 cm	0.0004	0.3	0.01	Cloud droplets
100 = 0.01 cm	0.004	30	1.0	Drizzle
1,000 = 0.1 cm	0.04	460	15	Rain

It can be seen that raindrops fall rapidly. By contrast, smoke and dust particles fall so slowly that they can be regarded as not falling at all. They are virtually suspended in the air and carried along with the air molecules. Rising currents of air transport them to high altitudes, mix them with clean air, and diffuse them through a greater portion of the atmosphere.

Of course, the particles thrown into the atmosphere will not stay there forever. As a matter of fact, it has been estimated that in a period of about two weeks the amount of dust and smoke particles removed from the atmosphere will just equal the total amount in the atmosphere. This is called *turnover* time. That is not to say that the atmosphere is completely flushed out and replenished with a new supply of aerosols. Rather, the rate of removal is such that if it continued undisturbed for the turnover time, it would clear out all the particles. Of course, the rate of replenishment is about the same as the rate of removal. Hence, the total supply of smoke and dust remains about the same—but not exactly the same. On the basis of reports from all over the world, it appears that the rate of addition slightly exceeds the rate of removal. The quantity of air pollution is gradually increasing.

We have remarked the fact that the fall speed of dust and smoke is so small that they can be regarded as not falling at all. How then do the small particles leave the atmosphere? This question will be dealt with more extensively in a later chapter, but we should note that they are swept out by larger particles, particularly rain and snow. Atmospheric scientists sometimes say that precipitation "scrubs the atmosphere" or "washes it out." You often see evidence of this when a very light rain falls on a windy, dusty day. The raindrops transfer the dirt from the atmosphere to the hoods and windows of automobiles and over other objects as well. Since this often seems to happen just after you've had the car washed, it is irritating, but it is probably better to have a dirty car than a dirty atmosphere.

Chapter IV

CAPTURING PARTICLES AND SAMPLING GASES

So far, we have said very little about the nature of particles in the air, except that they are small and numerous. You might justly ask, "How small? How numerous? What are they made of? How do you know these things?" Of course, the scientists working on atmospheric aerosols have at least as many questions as answers.

Most of the information about the properties of aerosols in the atmosphere has been obtained by capturing them and examining them in the laboratory. The capture of a tiny particle is not always an easy job. Many schemes have been conceived and tried. Some have been successful and are in use; others have gone by the boards.

As you would imagine, the best collection technique to be used in any instance depends to a certain extent on the size of the particles you want to capture. You might say that the size of the hook depends on the size of the fish. For relatively large particles, those with diameters greater than 0.5 micron or so, the fishing is relatively easy, and many techniques are available. As the particle diameters approach 0.1 micron and smaller, the number of collection devices becomes more limited.

Filtering

One of the oldest schemes for separating large things from smaller ones involves the use of filters or sieves. Sand is separated from gravel this way. Coffee grounds can be separated from the liquid with a filter. The most essential feature of any filter is that the hole sizes be such that all the substance below the desired size can pass through the filter while the other particles of greater size are held back. But that is not enough.

In a coffee pot, the water passes through the holes but the coffee grounds with diameters greater than the holes are held back. At first glance, it would appear that as long as the holes are smaller than the coffee grains, the percolator will do its job. But this is not really true. If the holes are too small, the flow of water will be so slow that it might take an hour or two for enough water to pass over the grounds to make the coffee. Eventually, you would have a pot of brown liquid resembling coffee in appearance at least, but it probably would not taste very good, and you would be late for work. You might say that the difficulty of the slow flow through the small holes could be overcome by making more holes. This is true enough, but it represents only a short-term solution. Small holes become clogged more quickly than the larger ones and, after a time, the filter would be completely useless.

In general, the characteristics of the coffee pot sieve are not very different from almost any other filter. You always have to consider the hole or *pore* size, as it is called, in relation to the size and quantity of the particles you wish to capture.

At times, scientists or engineers want to know the total quantity of particles of a type in a cubic meter of air. If you had reason for believing the particle diameters mostly to be greater than about a micron, you could use a common type of fiber filter. A known volume of air would then be pumped through the filter. The material on the filter would be removed in a chemical laboratory, analyzed, and weighed. Knowing how much the clean filter weighed, you then could compute easily how much particulate matter was collected.

The types of analytical techniques used to determine the chemical composition of the aerosols would be those normally employed when the quantities of materials are fairly large. This calls for something of the order of a thimbleful. It would not be possible to ascertain whether the individual particles were in the atmosphere in the form of a relatively few giant particles or were many more but smaller ones.

When you want to know the size of the individual particles you can use a filtering device of a special type. Called a membrane filter, it is made of a mixture of cellulose nitrate and acetate. As we shall see, this material has some interesting properties. One type of membrane filter is called Millipore. A commonly used size has uniform pores about 0.1 to 0.3 micron in diameter. The filter is white and appears to be a piece of soft paper, but it is mostly air. About 80 per cent of the surface area is open space between extremely fine fibers. But the fibers are so close you cannot see the air spaces between them. By pumping air through the Millipore, you can capture all particles larger than the pore size. Of course, if you do not plan your measurements with care, you might pump air long enough to coat the filter with particles and close up the pores. On the other hand, by restricting the quantity of filtered air, you can restrict the number of particles on the filter.

After the collection has been made, you can use various techniques to examine the particles, measure their size, and possibly identify their composition. Sometimes you can make a judgment of the nature of the particle from its shape, crystal properties, and color as viewed under a microscope. At other times it is necessary to perform certain chemical tests. The term *spot tests* is used to designate analyses of the properties of such particles.

Settling Devices

It is often of interest to know the quantities of particulate matter falling out of the air. The simplest scheme for learning the sizes and quantities of particles larger than a few microns involves the use of sampling slides or jars. They are placed in strategic positions and left alone. Instead of going out to find the particles, you let the particles come to you.

Surveys of the particulate output of refineries, power plants or, for that matter, any dust- or smoke-producing source can be made by placing jars downwind from the source for a given period of time—about a month or so. In view of the small expense involved, a great many jars can be used. The amount of fallout can be measured by careful weighing. With this information on hand, the effectiveness of a smokestack, for example, can be studied. The technique of fallout bottles is used by industrial groups, organizations such as the Public Health Service, and other agencies interested in air pollution.

It may appear that the amount of dust, smoke particles, and fly ash falling out of the air is too small to be measured accurately with the crude scheme of the fallout jar. However, it has been found that the average dustfall in large cities such as New York, Chicago, and Detroit has been greater than 50 tons per square mile per month. During some especially bad situations, it can be more than twice that much. It is a fact (painfully obvious to its inhabitants) that every large city is almost constantly being showered with a steady stream of dirt. People who live in the country or in smaller towns with little or no industrial activity may not realize the seriousness of the dustfall problem, but those who live in the large cities know. They see their cars covered with soot and other particles. They see dirt on their hands, faces, and clothing.

We have been considering the use of the fallout jar for getting bulk measurements of the falling aerosols. If you want to capture and study individual particles, you use glass or plastic slides coated with a sticky substance. When the grains hit, they are held until the analyst is ready to examine them in detail.

When the particles have diameters of less than about a micron, the likelihood of fallout on a slide exposed to the atmosphere is hard to estimate. The chances of particles' falling on the slide are very small and highly variable because they move largely with the wind. Consequently, if you wanted to know how many there were in a cubic meter of air, you would have to use some other scheme.

A relatively simple sedimentation technique employs a square box about one-half meter on the side. Several slides, perhaps four, are mounted on each of the six inner walls of the box. Then the air to be sampled is gently blown in. When this flushing job is finished, the box is closed and allowed to sit for periods of 12 to 24 hours. During this time, the particles migrate toward the walls and either settle or impact on them. Of course, some also fall on the glass slides. Knowing the size of the slides and the walls, you can estimate how many particles were in the known volume of air.

When a box with little or no insulation is used, the deposition of particles on various slides of the box may be different from what you might guess. Often, it is found that nearly as many particles hit and stick to the top of the box as to its floor. The chief cause of this appears to be so-called "convection currents" in the box. They are set up because the six sides of the chamber may not have the same temperature. The unequally heated air is set in motion because the warmer, less dense air rises while the cooler air sinks. The submicron particles closely follow the air except just near the walls, where a small deviation between air motion and particle motion allows the particle to strike and stick to the wall or one of the slides. Have you ever noticed that the ceiling is frequently dirtiest over radiators or hot air ducts? This condition also is caused by warm air rising in a convective current and carrying up particles which strike and stick to the cooler ceiling. (This seems to contradict what we said in Chapter I about the relative concentration of dirt on hot and cold walls, but here another factor is involved. The convection current acts to transport a greater number of particles upward and into contact with the ceiling.)

Impaction Techniques

When particles with diameters greater than about 0.5 micron are the subjects of interest, a whole new class of collecting devices becomes available—*impactors* or *impingers*. They are designed to bring about the collision of particles on a glass, plastic, or metal surface.

The operation of a device called a single-stage impactor is illustrated in Figure 6. Air containing the particles is drawn down the jet tube by means of a pump or, as is

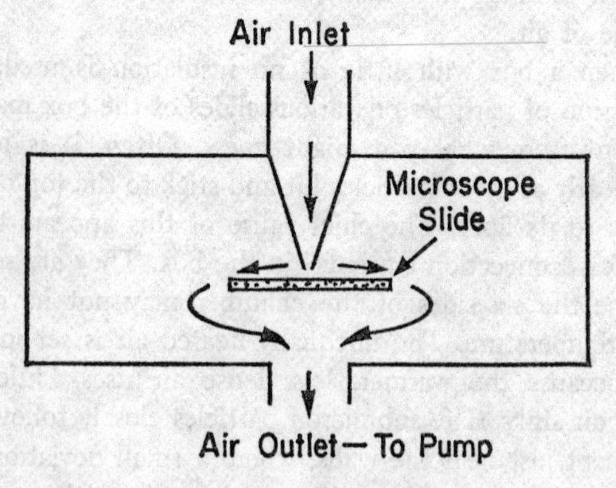

Fig. 6 Sketch of a single-stage impactor.

sometimes done in practice, by a vacuum cleaner. The tube is tapered down to a fine nozzle. It might be as small as 0.02 millimeter in diameter but at times is 5 to 10 times larger. Its size depends on the size of the particles to be collected. As the air passes through the nozzles it speeds up tremendously. In some cases it can approach the speed of sound. On striking the glass or plastic slide, a fraction of a millimeter away, the air is deflected in all directions, as shown in the illustration. The particles tend to be carried along by the air, but they have enough inertia that they do not follow exactly. This condition exists especially at places where the air motion curves sharply. The particles move across the air stream, strike the slide, and stick to it. When large aerosols are to be captured, the slide may be coated with a tacky substance capable of holding them in place.

When an impactor is designed, several features can be varied: (1) the size of the nozzle; (2) the distance between nozzle and slide; (3) the speed of the air. As you would expect, the smaller the particles to be collected, the smaller should be items (1) and (2) and the higher the air speed.

We mentioned at the outset of this section that impaction devices are useful when the particle diameters are greater than about 0.5 micron. Smaller particles follow the air even when it moves at extremely high speeds around 90-degree turns.

When an impactor is employed it is essential that you know what fraction of the particles moving through the nozzle is likely to be impacted. This fraction is measured by a quantity called the *impaction efficiency*. It is equal to the ratio of the number of particles of any size actually impacted to the number passing through the nozzle. The impaction efficiency can be calculated, but in general should be determined experimentally. Figure 7 illustrates

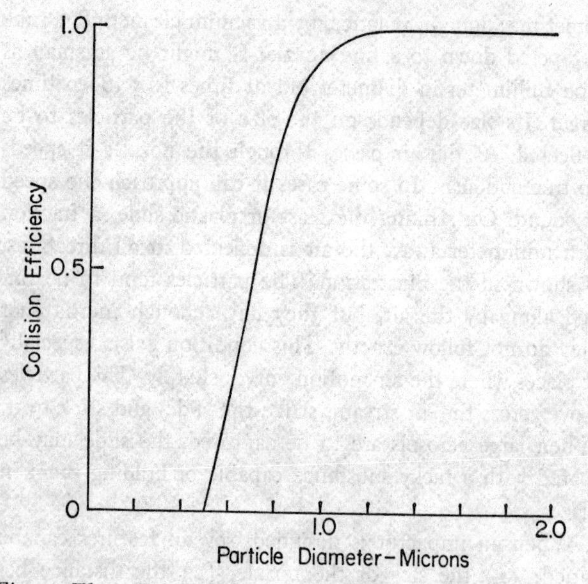

Fig. 7 The collision efficiency of an impactor measures the fraction of particles of any particular size which are collected by the impactor.

the appearance of a curve relating the efficiency to particle diameter. As you would expect, all large particles are collected. In this particular instance the efficiency drops sharply with particle diameters smaller than one micron, reaches 50 per cent at 0.7 micron, and zero at 0.5 micron.

A curve such as the one shown in Figure 7 is also called a "calibration curve" and is used to adjust the measurements obtained with the device. This is done in the following way: Let us imagine that a cubic centimeter of air has been sampled and is found to contain 100 particles with diameters of 1 micron and 75 with diameters of 0.7 micron. The curve tells us that the device will collect 100 per cent of the former but only 50 per cent of the latter. Thus we must correct the observed number of micron aerosols with diameter 75 microns by multiplying with a correction factor equal to two. In other words, we are led to the conclusion that in the one cubic meter of sampled air there were 150 particles having a diameter of 0.7 micron.

The single-stage impactor can be used with a glass slide, as shown in Figure 6. In some instances the chamber contains a strip of plastic or paper on a rotating drum just under the nozzle. If you know the rate of rotation of the drum you can observe how the aerosol content of the air changes with time. When white paper is used and the drum allowed to turn slowly, the impacted material may coat the paper sufficiently to give it varying shades of gray. By noting the change of shading, you can estimate how the quantity of pollution in the air is changing.

Measurements of the variations in time of individual particles have been made by employing a specially coated plastic strip wrapped around a rotating drum. It must be turned fast enough that the number of impactions will be relatively small so as to reduce the likelihood of having particles fall on top of one another.

There are some difficulties in employing a single-stage impactor to measure the distribution of particle sizes in the atmosphere. We have mentioned the cutoff of collections at about 0.5 micron. Another problem arises when particles with diameters as large as 5 to 10 microns are present. They usually occur in very small numbers, or to be more precise, in low concentrations. For example, in a sample of air near the ocean the concentration of sea-salt particles with diameters of about 0.5 micron might be about 100,000 per cubic meter. At the other end of the spectrum the concentration of 5-micron salt particles might be perhaps 100 to 1000 per cubic meter. The concentration of intermediate sizes would range between the two extremes given here. The wide range of concentration raises a serious sampling problem.

In order for a single-stage impactor to capture enough of

the larger particles to allow accurate estimates of the concentrations, it would have to "oversample" the small ones. This condition would have the effect of increasing the number of collisions of particles on the slide. Superimposition of particles would make it difficult to estimate the original sizes. If the air sample is decreased in order to reduce the area of the slide covered with particles, the number of large particles impacted may become so small as to be meaningless.

The specialists on aerosols have recognized these difficulties of the single-stage impactor, and have devised multi-staged impactors. Generally, the latter devices are called *cascade impactors* for reasons which will soon become apparent.

Figure 8 shows a sketch of one type of cascade impactor.

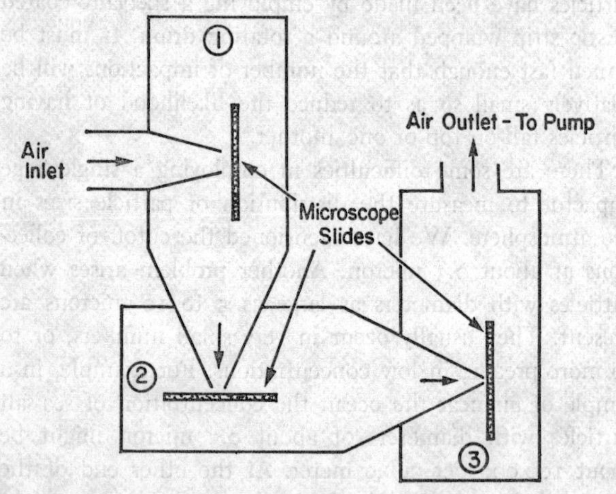

Fig. 8 Sketch of a three-stage impactor.

As you can see, it is actually three single-stage impactors arranged in series with one another. However, what you might not readily see is that they are slightly different in their design. Each of the individual impactors is intended to capture particles of a different size. The same air flows through all the impactors, as shown by the arrows on the illustration. The first stage, marked 1, is constructed to capture the larger particles, for example, those greater than 2 microns in diameter. This does not mean that every single particle greater than 2 microns is caught and all smaller ones missed. It means that the impaction efficiency curve drops sharply toward zero at diameters below about 2 microns. Most of the smaller aerosols pass through stage 1 unmolested and head for stage 2.

The impactor of stage 2 is designed for the capture of particles of intermediate size, those between 0.8 and 2.0 microns in diameter, for example. The nozzle size is smaller than in stage 1. Also smaller is the distance between nozzle and slide, and as a result at stage 2 the air speed is higher. The collection efficiency is near 100 per cent for particles having a diameter greater than about 0.8 micron. Most particles with diameters between 0.8 and 2.0 microns will impact on slide 2. Smaller particles pass on through stage 2. When stage 3 has been designed properly, aerosols with diameters between 0.5 and 0.8 micron are captured. As you have already surmised, the last impactor has still smaller nozzle size and nozzle-to-slide distance than the preceding one.

By means of cascade impactors it is possible to learn the range of aerosol sizes and numbers. The device we have just discussed is, for obvious reasons, a three-stage impactor. If more details are desired more stages are used. As many as five stages have been employed in a single device.

For obtaining small samples of aerosols it is possible to use a species of "impactor" very different from the ones we have been discussing. It has the advantage of being capable of intercepting particles smaller than 0.1 micron. Henri Dessens, in France, developed the technique. Rather than allowing the particles to impact on a relatively large surface, he decided to reduce the surface to virtually the minimal supportable value. In 1946, before the days of the extremely fine plastic fibers, Dessens looked to nature. He captured some spiders and put them to work.

For some reason most people are frightened of spiders and hesitant to handle them, even though most are harmless. Some of them, given the opportunity, have been quick to make a contribution to science. At one well-known laboratory with which the author was associated, a pretty female assistant almost resigned when she got the job of capturing some spiders which lived in vines climbing the building. She thought her job was to wash the glassware. It took some persuading to convince her that the creatures would not bite, but she carried out her assignment bravely.

Certain spiders spin a unique thread. It is very uniform in diameter and extremely fine, about 0.01 micron. In comparison, note that a human hair is about 100 microns in diameter. Once you have the spider, you let it spin a fiber, which is strung across a metal frame. In order to capture aerosols, the frame is held so that the air moves in a direction perpendicular to the threads. Because of their extreme fineness and sticky surface, the impaction efficiency of the threads is very high, even for very tiny particles. Particles with diameters smaller than 0.1 micron can be captured on the spider threads. As you might expect, this technique allows only few particles to be captured at any one time. The size and numbers are observed by mounting the supporting frame under a microscope.

Thermal and Electrostatic Precipitators

When particles are smaller than about 0.1 micron in diameter the most efficient collection techniques involve instruments called "thermal precipitators" or "electrostatic precipitators." In both devices, the air is passed between two nearby surfaces and forces are brought into play to drive the aerosols toward one surface.

Let us first consider the thermal device. We mentioned that the air molecules in hot air are in more violent motion than the molecules in cooler air. If a small dust particle passed between two surfaces having different temperatures it would be subject to bombardment by air molecules moving from all directions. But those coming from the direction of the warmer surface, on the average, would be moving with greater speed than those from the opposite direction. As a result, the particle would be driven toward the cooler surface. If the size of the particle and the spacing between hot and cold surfaces are small enough, the particle eventually impinges on the cooler surface. By means of an appropriately placed slide, the particle is captured and can be examined under a suitable microscope.

Electrostatic precipitators come in many sizes and are used for laboratory work as well as for commercial pollution-control purposes. They work on the principle that electric charges of the same sign repel, while opposites attract one another. Thus if a negatively charged particle passes between two metal plates having opposite charges, the particle will be attracted toward the positively charged plate. It can be said that the electrical forces cause the particle to precipitate on one of the plates.

An electrostatic precipitator contains a source of electrical ions which charge the aerosols. The source may be a wire with a high negative voltage. It is mounted close to, but insulated from, a positively charged metal plate. Between the wire and the plate there is a strong electrostatic field which drives the particles toward the positive plate. They may be captured by mounting a slide on the plate.

Aitkin Nuclei Counter

All the devices described so far involve the capture of particles on a filter, a slide, or a spider's thread. Let us examine one device which tells us about aerosols without capturing them.

The basic idea goes back to a British scientist, J. Aitkin, who worked on it about 1890. He found that when a volume of air was expanded suddenly, the resultant cooling* led to the formation of a cloud. He concluded that water vapor was condensing on particles in the air. Aitkin performed a large variety of experiments showing that the number of drops per unit volume depended on such factors as the properties of the nuclei, as well as on the amount of expansion. Up to a certain point, at least, the greater the expansion, the more dense the cloud. This work has been the basis for the so-called "Aitkin nuclei counter."

Over the years Aitkin's idea has been refined. Presently there are commercially available devices which perform known expansions and use a light beam and photocell to measure the cloud density. These instruments measure the particle concentration in the atmosphere.

The Aitkin counter can detect the presence of particles with diameters as small as 0.01 micron, about a tenth as small as those measured by the techniques discussed earlier. Unfortunately, however, it tells you almost nothing about the range of sizes of particles or their compositions. It gives information only about the concentration of particles. For this reason it has had relatively limited use.

* The reasons why expanding air cools will be explained in a later chapter.

Sampling Gases

There is a variety of methods for sampling the gases in the atmosphere. The most common method involves passing through a liquid which "scrubs" the air. By scrubbing we mean that the liquid reacts in some way with the gaseous contaminant and removes it from the air. The absorbing liquids are selected for their known capacities to react with specific gaseous impurities. For example, one liquid may collect sulfur dioxide, another hydrogen sulfide, and so forth. (In due course we shall discuss gases most detrimental to life and property. We shall find these two substances among them.) Once the liquid has absorbed the gas in question, there are chemical techniques for measuring the quantity of gas. Concentrations of smaller than one part of gas in 10 million parts of air can be evaluated by more or less standard analytical methods.

It is possible also to extract gas samples by passing air through filters made of materials, activated charcoal among them, which efficiently absorb the gas in question. It is necessary to be very careful in the selection of the absorbing material. After the collection, the gas can be removed from the solid by warming, collected and analyzed to determine its properties.

Another scheme for observing certain contaminating gases involves the use of solid material impregnated with a substance whose color changes when it is exposed to a particular type of gas. Various such devices have been designed for determining the presence of sulfur dioxide.

Chapter V

SOME CHEMISTRY OF THE ATMOSPHERE

The atmosphere is a huge reservoir of air speckled with clouds and dusted with particles of almost any conceivable composition. The weight of the entire atmosphere is about 6×10^{15} tons, that is, 6 with 15 zeros after it. Of this quantity about 78 per cent (by volume) is nitrogen, almost 21 per cent is oxygen, and almost 1 per cent argon. The remaining fraction of 1 per cent of dry air is made up of such gases as carbon dioxide, ozone, methane, and many others. We have not included that well-known substance water vapor because the term "dry air" means air with no water vapor.

When we say "air" we are talking really about a mixture of gases. Atmospheric scientists sometimes use the term "air molecules." From what we have just said, there can be no such thing. So why do they do it?

The reason for using the term "air molecules" is that the mixture of gases called "air" behaves as if it were a single gas. If you never studied chemistry, this statement needs further explanation.

Scientists have long made use of a concept known as Boyle's Law. This law states that when the temperature of a perfect gas is kept constant, the pressure multiplied by the volume is also constant. Thus, when the volume of a constant-temperature, closed cylinder is increased, perhaps by moving a piston, the pressure decreases. Conversely, when the volume decreases, the pressure increases. Strictly speaking, this law applies to a perfect gas, but when experiments are made with the mixture of gases called "air," we find it also follows Boyle's Law. Similarly, air also conforms to the behavior of perfect gases in other ways. For this reason, it is convenient to consider air a gas.

One important property of every substance is a quantity called its *molecular weight*. It is a measure of the weight of an element with respect to the weight of oxygen. For example, atomic hydrogen has a molecular weight of 1.008, while atomic oxygen, which is the standard, is 16.000. In the atmosphere oxygen is mostly in the form of molecules (O_2) containing two atoms and has a molecular weight of 32.000. Nitrogen, the most abundant gas in the atmosphere, is made up of molecules containing two atoms of nitrogen (N_2); it has a molecular weight of 28.016.

The substance we call "dry air" has been assigned a "molecular weight" of 28.9. You can easily calculate this number by assuming that air is, for this purpose, 78 per cent N_2 and almost 22 per cent O_2.

When a balloon is filled with hydrogen and released, it rises. The reason is almost obvious. You might say that it weighs less than the air and therefore it rises. It is more correct to say that it rises because an upward force is acting on it. The force is equal to the difference between the weight of the hydrogen in the balloon and air which it displaced. But how do you account for this difference in weight? You can do so by recognizing that the molecular weight of the hydrogen molecule H_2 is 2.016 while that of air is 28.9, about fourteen times greater. Of course, the hydrogen need not be inside the balloon to rise, but then it would mix with the other gases.

One of the most important substances in the atmosphere is water vapor. It gets there as a result of evaporation from oceans and lakes and all types of wet surfaces. Plants transpire (we say "perspire" for people) and thereby add tremendous quantities of water vapor to the atmosphere. Water vapor is removed from the atmosphere as a result of condensation, usually in the form of clouds of water droplets and ice crystals. They may eventually produce rain or snow and return the water to the earth's surface. Also, some water vapor leaves the atmosphere as dew on cool early mornings. On cold nights, frost may form on blades of grass, leaves, fences, and so on.

Unlike the gases we have already mentioned as the constituents of dry air, the amount of water vapor in moist air varies greatly from place to place and from time to time. In desert regions the quantity usually is small, as it is also in very cold air over large continents. At the other extreme, in warm air over the tropical oceans there are large amounts of water vapor. When large bodies of air from the tropical oceans move over land, the high humidities are easily observed. When it is hot and humid you know there is abundant water vapor. You feel uncomfortable. High temperatures cause you to perspire, the body's mechanism for cooling off. If the air is dry the evaporation from your skin lowers the skin temperature. But when the air is humid, when the relative humidity is high, evaporation proceeds very slowly. As a result, the sweat, instead of cooling you, wets you and contributes to further discomfort.

The quantity of water vapor in the air sometimes reaches as high as 3 per cent of the air volume. Most of the time it is less than 1 per cent.

What would you say is the molecular weight of water vapor? Is it heavier or lighter than dry air? Remember that the term "water vapor" means a gas of water molecules, not the cloud of water droplets found at the mouth of a tea kettle. A water molecule (H_2O) is composed of two atoms of hydrogen and one atom of oxygen. Therefore, its molecular weight is $2 + 16$, or 18. Thus water vapor is lighter than dry air, which we already noted has a molecular weight of almost 29. Furthermore, a given volume of a mixture of dry air and water vapor is lighter than the same volume of dry air alone.

For reasons already suggested, it is important to know the molecular weights of gases released into the atmosphere. Gases with weights less than that of air tend to rise. Heavier gases do not. Instead, they flow along the ground. Release of a gas that is both heavy and toxic calls for great care lest it produce a blanket of poison hugging the ground and flowing readily into the lungs of the unsuspecting, human or animal.

In addition to the nitrogen, oxygen, argon, and water vapor which together represent about 99.96 per cent of the volume of the atmosphere, there still are large quantities of other substances. The remaining 0.04 per cent has a mass of about 2×10^{12} tons, that is 2 million, million tons. It is not convenient to talk about such large numbers.

Atmospheric chemists customarily measure the quantities of gases or particulate matter in terms of parts per million of air. This is a useful device for those substances normally present in very minute but important quantities. They are often called "trace gases" or "trace impurities." Helium, for example, occurs in the atmosphere in concentrations of about 5 parts per million by volume. This means if all the air in a cubic meter could somehow be treated to separate out all the helium, the helium would occupy 5 cubic centimeters of the one million centimeters in the cubic meter.

At first glance it might appear that a gas in concentrations of only a few parts per million would be so dilute as to be harmless, but this is not always the case.

The History of Common Gases

The supply of nitrogen (N_2) in the atmosphere is virtually constant. Decaying plants, leaves, and animal matter release nitrogen. It is also exhaled from the earth in several ways. Volcanic eruptions throw large quantities of nitrogen into the air. Certain types of rocks release nitrogen. The burning of fuels containing nitrogen also contributes to the supply. On the other side of the ledger, nitrogen is extracted from the atmosphere in biological processes involving plants and sea life. To a less extent, lightning causes the formation of nitrogen compounds which are washed out of the atmosphere by rain and snow.

Oxygen (O_2) is another of the nearly constant gases. The major sources are the many plants exchanging carbon dioxide for oxygen. The atmosphere gives up oxygen to the seas, where it dissolves. Oxygen goes into the production of various compounds. For example, it reacts with iron to cause rusting. Human beings and animals do the reverse of the exchange in plants. We inhale oxygen and exhale carbon dioxide.

Carbon dioxide (CO_2) is present in the atmosphere in concentrations of about 300 parts per million by volume, about 2600 times less abundant than nitrogen. It appears that over geological time the quantity of carbon dioxide has not varied very much, but there have been fluctuations. In particular, since the turn of the century there has been an increase of about 5 per cent in the concentration. The reason generally given is the tremendous increase in the consumption of fossil fuels—coal, oil, and gasoline. These are the relatively new sources of carbon dioxide. The old ones are volcanoes and the rotting of all forms of organic matter, such as leaves, plants, and animals.

Fortunately, carbon dioxide dissolves readily in water and is taken up by most plants; otherwise, the increase in the atmosphere could have really serious consequences. Carbon dioxide efficiently absorbs some of the heat radiated from the earth and prevents it from escaping to outer space. On the other hand, it allows the sun's rays to penetrate to the earth. This means that as the CO_2 concentration rises the quantity of energy trapped near the earth increases slowly.

Over the last forty to fifty years there has been a small but important increase in the temperature around the world. It has amounted to an average rise of about a degree centigrade. But this small rise has been accompanied by retreat of glaciers, melting of the Arctic ice pack, and other such changes. It has been proposed that the warming may have come about because of the increase of carbon dioxide. This vital point is still under study. Continued warming and melting of polar ice could lead to catastrophes along low-lying coastlines. As the ice melts the sea level rises. Sufficient melting could lead to the flooding of large areas.

Everyone knows that without oxygen, human beings and animals would not survive. When we use the term "oxygen" in this sense, we mean a gas composed of molecules made up of two atoms of oxygen. As already noted, this gas is represented by the symbol O_2. Its quantity is fairly constant through a layer of perhaps 50 miles surrounding the earth. Its concentration is about 210,000 per million parts of air.

Oxygen atoms do not always combine in pairs to constitute the essential O_2. Sometimes three atoms combine to form a molecule of a gas called *ozone*, O_3. This substance, unlike its evidently more poorly endowed relative, O_2, is poisonous. Sufficiently high concentrations can kill you. Even small ones can irritate people and damage plants. Fortunately, most of the ozone is in the stratosphere at altitudes between about ten and thirty-five miles. Concentrations as high as 8 parts per million occur. This compares with average values near the ground of less than 0.07 in particular regions, such as Southern California, where concentrations have reached as high as 0.5 part per million on smoggy days. Over a period of half an hour, such a concentration can damage some plant life.

We just said how lucky we are that the greatest quantities of poisonous ozone are found in the upper atmosphere, away from living things on the earth. Not only is it too far from us to be dangerous, but also it protects us from another hazard. Ozone has the property of absorbing ultraviolet light.

If you went up to the high reaches of the atmosphere where these days the satellites move, you would be wise not to try to bask in the sunshine. If you did, you would get a sunburn to end all sunburns. The reason is not that you would be closer to the sun. You certainly would be, but only by a trivial amount when you remember that the sun is 93,000,000 miles away. The reason for the solar roasting is that you would no longer have the atmospheric gases and particles to filter out and reduce the intensity of the sun's rays.

Ozone in particular is active in absorbing some of the sun's rays. At the top of the atmosphere sunlight contains a substantial amount of energy known as ultraviolet. It gets this name because of the place it occupies in the color spectrum. When a rainbow occurs you see that it is made up of a regular series of colors starting from red on the outside and going to orange, yellow, green, blue, and violet. These colors come from sunlight. A rainbow is produced when a rain shower intercepts sunlight and reflects it back to your eyes. The raindrops, acting like small prisms, separate the various colors. It is possible to explain how this comes about if light is considered to be made up of waves of different lengths.

Most of the energy from the sun is contained in the wave length between about 0.00001 and 0.0003 centimeter. But the human eye cannot see them all. As a matter of fact, it can see only those ranging from about 0.00004 to 0.00007 centimeter, the former corresponding to violet and the latter to red light. The waves with lengths just below 0.00004 (that is, just below the violet) are the ones called ultraviolet. They are just beyond the short end of the visible limit. Even if we were above the atmosphere they would be invisible to the naked eye.

As the ultraviolet radiation passes through the ozone layer, much of the energy is absorbed by the ozone. This process warms up the air and produces a layer of high temperature at an altitude of about 35 miles. Since the ultraviolet is absorbed, very little reaches the ground. It has been estimated that if the ozone screen were not there, sunburn would occur more than 50 times faster than it does now under even the hottest summer sun. Further, the ultraviolet rays could have important detrimental effects on many biological processes on the earth.

Without a doubt, life on earth has adapted to the high-level blanket of ozone and has prospered under its shadow. Near the earth it is essential that the quantity of ozone be small. The sources of this gas at low altitudes are both local and external. There is evidence that some is transported down from the upper atmosphere in certain types of weather situations. In some cases it is formed on the scene in the same way as it is in the stratosphere. It is produced by the actions of sunlight and chemical reactions involving molecular and atomic oxygen.

Looking into the very near future, it is clear that we need to know much more about the ozone layer. The supersonic transport airplanes expected to be in service during the 1970's will be flying at the altitudes where ozone concentrations are high. It will be necessary to prevent ozone from entering the cabin. This does not appear to be too difficult, but another item of concern is the effect of ozone on rubber. Modern airplanes use rubber for a variety of purposes such as insulation on wiring, sealers for the windows, and, of course, in the giant tires. Ozone attacks rubber. It causes it to crack. As a matter of fact, a simple means for measuring ozone concentrations is to stretch a piece of rubber tubing and note how long it takes to crack.

Meteorologists all over the world have been giving increased attention to the measurement of ozone amounts in the atmosphere.

Some Unwanted Gases

In addition to those gases already mentioned there are many others whose presence usually goes unnoticed except to the curious eye of the expert. Of course, the word "eye" is not to be taken literally. Some of the trace gases such as xenon and krypton occur in concentrations of less than one part per million. They are not readily measured. They are in the class of elements known as "inert." This means they do not react readily with other substances. As a consequence, they have little effect on other gases or living things inhabiting the earth.

Still another category of gases remains to be mentioned. They have been left to the last because they are the ones with the greatest potential danger. For the most part they are added to the air by man and his occupations.

As we have indicated several times, the major sources of the unwanted gases are found in the cities. It is here that the greatest concentrations of people exist with their stoves, furnaces, factories, refineries, smelters, and engines, and, most of all, the automobile engine. All these things and others like them burn fossil fuel—coal, oil, gasoline, kerosene. In so doing they emit smokes. But serious problems arise because the fires do not completely burn the fuel.

Some gases inevitably escape into the atmosphere, and it is these gases which do the damage to eyes, throats, lungs, to plants of many varieties, and even to such seemingly indestructible things as metal and stone. The three substances leading to most of the noxious and toxic gases are sulfur, some nitrogen compounds, and so-called "hydrocarbons."

Sulfur dioxide is one of the important gaseous by-products flowing out of the chimneys of coal-burning furnaces. Some steps can be taken to remove it, but if this is not done, sulfur dioxide may be produced at a rate of perhaps one ton for every 10 tons of coal consumed. It occurs in quantities of several parts per million (p.p.m.) in large industrial cities. Concentrations exceeding about 6 p.p.m. can cause irritation of the nose and throat. Sulfur dioxide is considered by some authorities to have been the major culprit in the London, Donora, and Meuse Valley disasters mentioned earlier.

When sulfur reacts with water it produces a solution of H_2SO_4, the well-known sulfuric acid. As it falls to the ground in rain or, more important, when it is in the form of fog droplets floating through the air, the solution can erode metal, paint, and even stone. Sulfuric acid droplets also cause the rapid aging and breakdown of nylon hosiery.

The automobile is the chief source of the hydrocarbons in the atmosphere. Any time the engine fails to burn up the gasoline completely, some of the fumes are blown out the exhaust pipe. When racing down the open highway at high speed, the combustion efficiency of the engine is relatively high, but in city driving, even on the freeways, there are frequent changes of the throttle setting. Every time you step on the gas or lift your foot off the pedal, you change the degree of combustion and make an added contribution to the amount of gasoline fumes. Incidentally, you also supply an added quantity of carbon monoxide to the atmosphere.

When hydrocarbons get into the air on a sunny day, they react with the gases known as nitrogen oxides and produce a large number of strange gases. Not very much is known about them, but in concentration of a few parts per million of air they can start irritating eyes. In greater concentrations they can be lethal. It has been estimated that in Los Angeles somewhere in the vicinity of 1000 tons of hydrocarbons are poured into the air every day by automobiles alone. Of course, other sources such as garages, dry cleaning plants, etc., also make contributions.

A third important class of gaseous impurities are those already mentioned, nitrogen oxides. They occur by a combination of nitrogen and oxygen in a combustion process carried out at high temperatures. The cylinders of a high-powered automobile provide ideal conditions. Nitrogen dioxide is made up of one atom of nitrogen and two of oxygen. It is a reddish-brown gas known to be poisonous. In sufficient quantities this gas is lethal. This was proved dramatically in a fire in a Cleveland hospital some years ago, when X-ray film caught fire and released nitrogen dioxide in sufficient quantities to kill 125 people.

In the exhaust of an automobile engine the concentration of nitrogen oxides can be as high as 5000 parts per million. Naturally, the gases spread through the surrounding atmosphere so that the measurements taken in the free air in a large city may be only about one part per million or less. But clearly as the number of vehicles increases the quantity of gases also increases. Furthermore, since the reservoir for these unwanted gases remains about the same, the concentrations are bound to rise.

Several other gaseous impurities deserve to be mentioned. Hydrogen sulfide, with the stench of rotten eggs, is released from certain industrial plants, such as tanneries and rayon plants. You can detect the presence of concentrations as low as 0.1 p.p.m. by the characteristic smell, but such levels are seldom observed. However, even in smaller quantities hydrogen sulfide has corrosive effects on some paints.

Certain compounds of fluorine and chlorine are found in the atmosphere in sufficient amounts to be regarded as pollutants. They are produced mostly in specialized chemical plants and are of concern in localities where such plants exist.

Particle Composition

In earlier chapters we discussed some of the properties of particles in the air. Among the well-known ones are water droplets, soot, sand, and sea-salt particles. In this section let us consider some of the less familiar ones.

The automobile is already one of the chief villains of this story because of the gases it produces. It also adds particles to the atmosphere. Very large numbers of tiny solid grains ranging in diameter from about 0.02 to 0.06 micron and smaller numbers of larger sizes are commonly found in the exhaust gases. On the average the mass of solid matter equals about 0.08 per cent of the mass of gasoline consumed in the engine.

It has been found that about half of the particulate matter in the automobile exhausts is in the form of lead. Other substances contained in solid matter are chlorine, bromine, and carbon. Lead, chlorine, and bromine are added to gasoline in order to increase its octane rating and improve engine performance. The lead is mostly in the form of chemical compounds involving the substances just mentioned. Little has been written about the effects, if any, of those lead-bearing particles on human health.

Automobiles, trucks, buses, etc. also contribute large quantities of rubber to the atmosphere. Spinning, skidding, and slipping tires are slowly but steadily ground down. An average tire may last perhaps two or three years, and go from a finely chiseled and beveled ring of hard clean rubber to a completely bald and brittle candidate for the junk heap. It has been estimated that the streets of Los Angeles can rub about 50 tons of rubber off motor vehicle tires every day. Some of this quantity is vaporized, but much of it is in the form of tiny pieces of rubber.

W. L. Faith* has presented a list of twenty-one sub-

* *Air Pollution Control.* John Wiley & Sons (1959).

stances found in the form of particulate matter in the atmosphere over downtown Los Angeles in November 1954. Such substances as the following were most plentiful: lead, iron, magnesium, sodium, potassium, sulfates, nitrates, organic matter, and hydrocarbons. It is common to find individual particles made up of a mixture of two or more substances.

The concentration of solid matter averaged about 0.0005 grams per cubic meter of air, a value which seems quite small but certainly is not. Over an area one mile square in a layer 1000 feet thick there would be about 870 pounds of particulate matter.

If it all fell out in one day, the monthly fallout rate would be about 13 tons per square mile per month. In large cities such as Chicago and New York, values twice as large as this are not unusual.

There Is Much More to Know

In this discussion of the particles and gas in the air, we have not tried to be comprehensive, but rather to give you some notion of the great variety of substances found in vapor, solid, and liquid form. The reader who wants to know more about the chemistry of the atmosphere is urged to dig into the references listed at the end of this book.

Chapter VI

THE PRICE OF POLLUTION

Air pollution is costly in many ways. One obvious effect is that it dirties the sky and hides the beauties of nature and man. The mountain peak is not magnificent nor the skyline breathtaking when it is enveloped in a cloud of unwanted aerosols.

Numerous references have been made to instances where contaminated air damaged property, injured plants, animals, and people, and sometimes even killed them. For quite a few years, scientists have been trying to find out specifically which substances are the damaging ones. In London in the great smog people breathed many lungfuls of smoky air. Most people, though unhappy about the look, smell, and taste, showed no ill effect. Others got sick and a large number died. The air contained many substances, but the important still-unanswered question is: Which substance or substances should be blamed for the tragic results?

Questions such as this one are in urgent need of reliable answers. Until satisfactory answers are obtained, how can one efficiently plan corrective measures? How does one treat the afflicted?

We know that in polluted air in a large industrial city there are a great many different gases and particles. Some occur in the minutest traces, incapable of doing harm. Others, of course, are dangerous to all living matter. Obviously, all is not mystery. A great deal has been learned about the ways by which air pollution takes its toll. Later in this chapter we shall briefly review some aspects of this problem, but first let us consider how particles in the sky impair our seeing.

The Disappearing Nature

When air is clean and dry you can see for more than a hundred miles. As the atmosphere becomes polluted with smoke, dust, haze, and fog the transparency of the air decreases. Another way of saying the same thing is that the visibility decreases. In many industrial cities the visibility is commonly below 10 miles. When haze, smoke, and fog accumulate, visibility can shrink until it is only a matter of yards.

Technically, "visibility" is defined as the greatest distance at which it is just possible to see and identify an object with the naked eye. During the daytime a dark object against the sky is viewed; at night a moderately intense light is examined. Meteorologists usually use such objects as mountains, buildings, or towers in daylight and street lights or other such sources at night. Sometimes the visibility varies from one direction to another because of differences in the condition of the air.

In the last decade or so instruments called *transmissometers* have been developed for measuring visibility over relatively short distances.

Visibility is reduced whenever there are particles in the air. Rain and snow certainly act in this direction. The more common and serious obstructions are fog, haze, and smoke —the substances enhanced by polluted air.

Fog is made up of water droplets numbering a few hundred per cubic centimeter and of sizes ranging from a few microns to a few tens of microns. As a typical size let us say they are a few tenths the diameter of a human hair. The droplets form when water vapor condenses on smaller particles called "condensation nuclei."

Fog forms only when the relative humidity of the air is

high. This state of affairs can come about in various ways. When air is cooled at night as heat waves are radiated outward through clear skies, the relative humidity rises. The same thing happens when warm air moves over a colder surface and loses heat to the surface. There are other ways in which the air can be humidified, but these are two of the most common.

When the relative humidity approaches 100 per cent, water vapor condenses on condensation nuclei and a fog begins to appear. However, the fog sometimes forms even when the relative humidity is far below 100 per cent. This occurs when certain types of particles pollute the air. For example, when sea-salt particles are present, water molecules condense on them at relative humidities of about 75 per cent or so. We see persistent fogs of this sort along seacoasts.

Acid particles such as sulfuric or nitric acid also attract water molecules and grow readily to form fog droplets.

Sometimes even when the supply of acid particles and sea-salt is abundant, the relative humidity is still not high enough to lead to fog. The concentration of aerosols may be sufficient to create what is called a "haze." At times the particles may absorb water molecules but not in sufficient quantities to produce water droplets. A haze is made up of either dry particles or wet ones. They are very small—a few tenths of a micron in diameter—and cannot be seen with the naked eye. Nevertheless, they can interfere with visibility.

The third pollutant reducing visibility is smoke. Fine solid soot and ash particles are thrown into the air when burning occurs. Often smoke occurs together with haze or with fog.

Particles in the air reduce visibility by reflecting and absorbing the light. You see a mountain because the light reflected by the mountain reaches your eye. If the air is clear the light rays travel straight and undisturbed, but when aerosols are present they interfere with the light rays. Each aerosol absorbs a minute quantity of light energy. In addition, it reflects a much greater amount of the incident light in all directions. This effect is usually called "scattering." Although each particle, by itself, has little effect on the light ray, the sum of the effects of the billions upon billions of particles can profoundly influence the behavior of light waves. For example, a thundercloud can completely obscure the sun because the cloud droplets scatter and absorb most of the sunlight.

Clearly, the effects of the particles depend on their composition, on how many there are, and on their sizes. The more particles there are, the greater is the obstruction. Thus the greater the pollution the worse the visibility.

The serious nature of a dense fog is obvious to everyone. It is particularly important for those people who have to travel. All forms of transportation are slowed down or interrupted completely. Airplane travel is particularly affected. But fog need not be extremely dense to do this. As the visibility decreases, airplane landings are slowed down. When it gets below a mile, the rate of landings and takeoffs is seriously reduced.

You can imagine many ways in which poor visibility can affect human activity. One should be mentioned specifically because it often does not get enough emphasis. Air pollution makes the earth a less pleasant place to live. It reduces the beauty of nature. This blight is particularly noticed in mountain areas. Views that once made the pulse beat faster because of the spectacular panorama of mountains and valley are more often becoming shrouded in smoke. When once you almost always could see giant boulders sharply etched in the sky and the tapered arrowheads of spired pines, you now often see a fuzzy picture of brown and green. The polluted air acts like a translucent screen pulled down by an unhappy God.

You might say, "You are exaggerating! You make it appear that the earth is shrouded with a permanent layer of obscuring stuff." True, it is an exaggeration to say the air is always polluted. But it is not stretching the fact at all to note that in certain places the conditions described happen often enough to be noticed. Also, it is happening more often over more places than ever before. Air pollution has been getting worse. With each passing year the effects become more noticeable to almost every one of the human senses.

There is no ground for believing that the situation will get any better unless corrective measures are taken. Yesterday we saw the mountains, today only the valley. What about tomorrow?

Deteriorating Materials

A good qualitative measure of degree of air pollution is the color of your collar at the end of the day. Of course, if you work in an air-conditioned office or in a coal mine, this scheme does not work well at all. But in the days when there was no air conditioning the dark ring was an indication of how much dirt there was in the air.

There are other common indices of air pollution. How often does your house need painting? Or the car need washing?

The damage inflicted on a large variety of materials by polluted air is enormous. It has been estimated that in the United States the total could exceed a billion dollars every year. The major loss comes from damage to building stone, metals, fabrics, leather, paper, paint, and rubber.

Certain stones used in buildings, notably limestone, deteriorate when the air has abnormally high concentrations of carbon dioxide. If the humidity is high, carbonic acid can be produced, and the resulting reaction can discolor the stone. Rain then may wash away the surface, leaving it scarred and unattractive. Certain sulfur-bearing pollutants can have similar effects.

When air is moist, sulfur dioxide can react with the water molecules and create sulfuric acid mists. They can do extensive damage to steel. Sulfur-bearing substances turn copper surfaces green. The green layer actually is made up of a substance called copper sulfate. Fortunately, once the sulfate forms, it protects the copper metal from further deterioration.

Sulfur oxides and the sulfuric acid they produce cause deterioration in such substances as textiles and paper, which become brittle. Leather too is weakened.

It takes only small quantities of hydrogen sulfide gas to discolor badly any surface that has been coated with a paint containing lead. And every householder is sadly familiar with the dirt from soot and other dark particles which strike and stick to the walls and ceilings.

Ozone attacks textiles and rubber. It can discolor dyes of various kinds, including those in colored fabrics. We have mentioned that ozone causes stretched rubber to crack.

A very important and costly effect of air pollution is the one mentioned at the start of this section: namely, its dirtying of clothing, homes, automobiles, and so forth. The annual cleaning bills are staggering and are certainly far greater in a large industrialized city than in rural areas remote from major sources of air pollution.

Plant Damage

It is only in recent decades that people have begun to worry about the effects of air pollution on human health, but the effects on plants have been matters of concern for over a hundred years. The damage ranges from relatively minor injury to complete destruction. It depends on the type and condition of plants, on the kinds of pollutants as well as on their concentration and persistence.

In one sense, plants suffer because they "breathe." Poison gases enter their systems through openings in the leaves. A careful examination of a leaf shows it is made up of layers of matter having somewhat different properties (Figure 9). One surface is made up of a uniform,

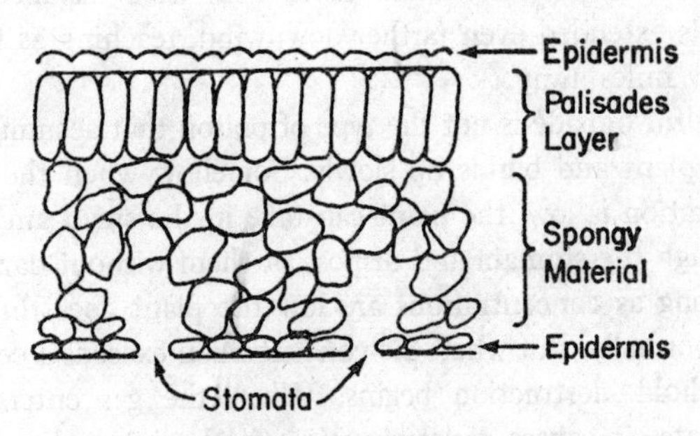

Fig. 9 Sketch of the cross section of a leaf.

hard, thin layer called the *epidermis,* or skin. The other surface of a leaf also is covered with epidermis but it has holes in it. These holes are called *stomata.* They are the "breathing tubes." The stomata open when it is hot, and water vapor escapes to the air. When this happens we say the plant *transpires.* To some degree, when a human being perspires the same purpose is accomplished. Transpiration and perspiration act to cool the plant and the man, respectively. When it gets cooler the stomata of the plant close and the plant loses water vapor slowly.

The noxious gases in the atmosphere enter the plants through the stomata and damage the internal structure of the leaves. Different gases may act somewhat differently, but the end result may be the same. Among the most toxic gases are sulfur dioxide, hydrogen fluoride, and ozone, the three gases which also damage materials. Chlorine, nitrogen dioxide, hydrogen chloride, and other gases also can be harmful if they occur in sufficiently high concentrations.

Sulfur dioxide is one of the worst culprits. Near Ducktown, Tennessee, sulfur dioxide downwind from industrial plants killed the plants and chemically affected the soil to the extent that now, fifty years later, the area still is virtually bare. Two copper smelters with short smokestacks started the trouble. When taller ones were installed the effects extended even farther downwind, reaching as far as thirty miles away.

Sulfur dioxide is not the type of poison that accumulates in a plant and builds up slowly. Somehow when the concentration is low, the plant can take in the small amounts through the stomata and dispose of them without damage. As long as concentrations are low the plant goes through life normally. But when the concentration exceeds a certain threshold destruction begins. When the gas enters the stomata, it causes a deterioration of the internal cells of the leaf. At first affected sections get blotchy and dry. With time all the solid part of the leaf may be affected, leaving only the veins in the form of a green skeleton. Then the veins also dry up, change in color from green to tan, and finally die.

As you might expect, sensitivity to sulfur dioxide differs from one plant to the next. Such common ones as alfalfa, cotton, lettuce, and spinach are among the most delicate. Elm, peach, apricot, and plum trees are of intermediate sensitivity. Cantaloupe, live oak, and privet are among the most resistant. It is not possible to generalize about which plants are weak and which are tough. If you want to know about any particular plant you have to look it up in the appropriate reference book.

Fluoride gases, unlike sulfur dioxide, are cumulative in their effects. Small concentrations over long periods can damage certain plants. When a gas such as hydrogen fluoride enters the stomata it causes the internal structure of the leaf to collapse. Visible damage starts at the ends and edges of the leaves and works inward. The affected parts dry out and become tan or brown. As the damage advances, the brittle pieces fall off, giving the leaf a broken appearance.

Ozone attacks the upper half of the leaf just under the skin. Distinctive spots, interestingly arranged in a band across the leaf, appear. Certain types of smog gases attack the lower part of the leaf just inside the stomata and also cause bands of damage across the leaves.

Leaf damage of these sorts is the visible effect of contaminating gases. It is not possible to say how much injury they may do to the productivity of the plants themselves, except in those cases where serious deterioration of the whole plant is involved. For example, how much smaller is the yield of peaches from a tree "breathing" contaminated air? Little is known about the internal wounds and scars left after a bout with pollution. The amount of damage to plant life and growth is hard to evaluate, but at least one estimate puts it in the hundreds of millions of dollars every year in the United States.*

Animals and Air Pollution

Man has suffered and continues to suffer at the hands of the contaminated air. What about his best friend—the dog? For that matter, how about the other pets often found around the house?

Following the Donora disaster described in the first chapter, a survey was made to see how the animals had been affected. It was found that canaries suffered the most. The experts were not surprised because this bird is known to be susceptible to respiratory problems. They were

* C. Stafford Brandt, "Effects of Air Pollution on Plants," *Air Pollution*. Academic Press (1962), pp. 255–81.

surprised, however, to find that dogs were next most seriously affected because dogs usually can breathe a great deal of foul air without injury. However, there is some question about the reliability of the reports on the dogs, so judgment on their response to polluted air has to be withheld.

Next in line of the most seriously affected at Donora were fowl, followed by cats. Pigeons and barnyard animals, cattle, horses, sheep, and pigs apparently were not affected.

In the great London smog of 1952 the results were somewhat different. During its presence, a large cattle show was in progress and a collection of prize beef was gathered in the city. Out of a total of 351 animals, 52 developed severe afflictions attributed to the smog. A total of 14 either died or had to be slaughtered and were found to have suffered respiratory or heart damage. There was no report of lethal effects on London's horses, but there was an increase of lung troubles among the monkeys at the zoo. As with people, the very young, the old, and the sick suffered the most.

In the Meuse Valley smog it was reported that cattle suffered from respiratory difficulties and some had to be slaughtered.

Unfortunately, no one knows for sure exactly which gas did the most damage in the three disasters. It is strongly suspected that sulfur dioxide was the chief villain. But there is only indirect evidence that this was the case. Satisfactory observations of pollutants were not made during the smog.

It is known that sulfur dioxide causes difficulties in the respiratory system of laboratory animals. As with plants, the concentration must exceed a certain threshold before any damage occurs. The critical value depends on the species. Guinea pigs are found to be very sensitive, rats the least sensitive. But even guinea pigs have been found to tolerate concentrations of 50 p.p.m. for about 6 to 7 hours per day for 30 days. Since the maximum concentrations of sulfur dioxide in a large city usually do not exceed about 1 p.p.m., it has been concluded that sulfur dioxide alone in normal concentration is not likely to have injurious effects on animals. Of course, in those cases where the concentration is much greater than normal, the consequences can be serious.

Although there is some question about the doses of ozone and nitrogen dioxide needed to cause injury to animals, there is no doubt that in sufficiently high concentrations they can cause lung troubles and even death.

It has been found that various gases which have little effect when breathed alone can cause serious difficulties when breathed as a mixture. In particular, substances found in smoggy air, ozone for example, when mixed with certain other gases, constitute a mixture which, in small doses, can kill rats. Sometimes the combination of gases works the other way around and the product is less toxic than either of the gases taken separately. Apparently not very much is understood yet about why the mixtures behave as they do.

People and Pollution

The importance of clean air to health has been stated in an unusual way by John R. Goldsmith.† He has pointed out that, in round numbers, a man can live 5 weeks without food, 5 days without water, but only 5 minutes without air. He also noted that each day an average man requires about 2.8 pounds of food, 4.5 pounds of water, but 30 pounds of air. As the "air" passes in and out of the lungs it undergoes changes. Oxygen is taken out of it, carbon dioxide is added to it. That process certainly occurs, but other things happen too.

† J. R. Goldsmith, "Effects of Air Pollution on Humans," *Air Pollution*. Academic Press (1962), pp. 336–86.

Inhaled air may contain all the gases and particles we have been talking about. The larger particles are trapped in the nose or throat. Some of the gases react with the fluids in the same places. But then the air carrying the oxygen as well as the remaining undesirable gases and particles floods the lungs. When a person exhales, some of the gases and particles do leave. The very tiny particles tend to move with the air and out they go. But some of the particles of intermediate size stay in the lungs and may start an ugly chain of events leading to serious illness and death. Certain gases can do the same.

Human lungs can be seriously affected in various ways. In some cases emphysema, a deterioration of cellular matter, is produced or aggravated. In other instances the coating of particles of many descriptions may interfere with the main function of transporting oxygen from the atmosphere to the bloodstream. It is suspected that some pollutants can start the growth of lung cancer.

Respiratory ailments that interfere with the normal flow of air in and out of the lungs put a strain on the pumping system—the heart. When the organ is already weak from other afflictions, one more strain may be too much. It is here that air pollution attacks the old and the very young who have little strength. Those who are both sick and aged are particularly likely to be struck down.

Sometimes death's sickle slashes with frightening suddenness, as it did in London in 1952. The concentration of poisons, in a matter of days, climbs steeply above the lethal level. Coughs begin, breath stops, and it's over. Other times, as a matter of fact most of the time, the effects are slow and invisible. Like moss growing up a forgotten wall, particles spread on the walls of the lungs. By the time the infection is discovered, it is so entrenched that it cannot be cured completely.

The human eye is an often hit and sensitive target of the atmospheric poisons. Fortunately, the eye has a built-in sprinkler system. When something gets into it and causes irritation, the tear ducts open and bathe the eyeball with quantities of liquid. Without this relief there would be many more blind people around than there are today. One of the most common complaints about smog is that it irritates the eyes and causes them to flow. The tears lead to other problems. Have you ever tried driving down the street while crying? First, your eyes go out of focus. Second, the tears running down your cheek tickle and there is the annoying fact that if you don't wipe them away they will drip on your clothes. Who can see well while his finger is in his eye?

Smog in the eyes doesn't approach lung problems as a serious threat to health but it has driven many people from the cities where it occurs often.

The gases most dangerous to people are, as you might expect, the same ones that threaten animals and plants—sulfur dioxide, nitrogen dioxide, ozone, so-called "smog gases" made up of complex mixtures of hydrocarbons. These are the gases generally found in industrialized cities with a great deal of motor traffic.

You may wonder about carbon monoxide, the common and well-publicized effluent from the tail pipes of automobiles. Every year many people die because they have run the engine in a closed garage or because leaking exhaust systems have allowed the deadly gas to enter cars with closed windows. There is no question that in heavy concentrations it is deadly; it attacks the hemoglobin in the blood and prevents it from transporting oxygen from the lungs to the tissue of the body. Nevertheless, it is believed that most of the time the amount of carbon monoxide in the open air is too low to do much damage to human health.

Hydrogen sulfide is another deadly gas when it occurs in large concentration. As you may recall, it has the distinctive odor of rotten eggs. You might think that this serves as a good warning signal. Unfortunately, you can smell it when it is present in small, safe quantities as well as when the concentrations are high. But after exposure to large concentrations of 100 parts per million or more for some minutes, the sensation of smell is lost. You could be enveloped in a cloud of the foul-smelling, death-dealing gas and not even know it. Luckily, even in polluted cities, maximum concentrations are generally far below the levels at which human health is endangered.

Nevertheless, hydrogen sulfide does represent a potential hazard in some types of industrial plants. In November 1950, a plant in Poza Rica, Mexico, which was extracting sulfur from natural gas, had a serious accident. By mistake, hydrogen sulfide gas (molecular weight = 34.1) was accidentally released into the air on a stable, foggy night. It was about 5 A.M. and most of the residents of the town were sleeping. The heavy, deadly gas flowed silently down the street, into houses, then into bedrooms. The victims found themselves inundated by an unseen fluid which choked them. There was no escape; they had to breathe. The gas attacked the respiratory and nervous systems. That night 320 people were hospitalized and 22 died as a result of the hydrogen sulfide poisoning. Such industrial disasters are rare and can be prevented by proper plant management.

Of the common gaseous pollutants, sulfur dioxide is regarded as one of the most dangerous to human health. It attacks the respiratory tract and interferes with the breathing mechanism. Concentrations above about 1 p.p.m. can begin to affect people. Some persons can stand more than five times as much. As you might expect, people with such ailments as bronchitis are the easiest prey.

In sufficient quantities nitrogen dioxide gas may attack the lungs. Also, it is considered to be a major factor in causing eye irritation. Some hydrocarbons and nitrogen dioxide under the influence of sunlight produce complex substances affecting the eye. The requirement of sunlight explains why the most serious eye problems occur in the daylight hours.

Solid particles transport dangerous substances. Certain particles containing carbon, soot for example, absorb substances known to produce cancer in laboratory animals. Breathed into the lungs, the particles may be deposited on the walls where they may eventually plant the seed of lung cancer. Autopsies on people exposed to smoky atmospheres have revealed lungs blackened with coated soot particles.

Aerosols–solid and liquids–also are carriers of sulfur, nitrogen, and hydrocarbons. In this form they may be drawn deep into the lungs.

There is no question that impure air is a health problem of great and increasing magnitude. The number of people afflicted with lung ailments such as emphysema, bronchitis, and asthma has been steadily increasing. Air pollution is at least part of the cause. More serious increases in these and related diseases surely can be expected unless positive steps are taken to reduce the pollutants entering the atmosphere. Equally important is the need to recognize and monitor the most dangerous ones. Finally, the atmosphere itself must be better understood, so that knowledge of its processes can be used to reduce the danger.

Chapter VII

WHAT MOVES THE AIR

If the earth had no atmosphere there would be no air pollution problem. Our moon is spared this affliction; hence, we can see its surface so clearly. Of course, the absence of air makes the moon a barren place with, as far as we know, no life of any kind. For life to develop and thrive there must be an atmosphere.

The atmosphere can be thought of as a fluid capable of supporting gases and particles and moving them from place to place. When the movement is small, the contaminating substances can accumulate. To understand and ultimately to solve the air pollution problem, it is necessary to understand the behavior of the atmosphere.

Depth of the Atmosphere

The earth's atmosphere, as was mentioned earlier, is made up of a mixture of many gases, but mostly of nitrogen and oxygen. The smaller quantities of ozone, carbon dioxide, and water vapor are vital in the maintenance of plant and animal life. The still smaller quantities of a great many other gases affect the earth's environment in wonderful and sometimes mysterious ways.

It may seem sometimes that the air is just weightless empty space, but we know otherwise. The pressure exerted by the air at the surface of the earth averages about 14.7 pounds per square inch. A column of air an inch in cross section extending to the top of the atmosphere weighs 14.7

pounds. You might ask, why can't we feel it pressing down on our bodies? The answer is easy. Pressure has the property of having the same magnitude in all directions. Thus inside your body there is an equal and opposite pressure to that outside it. The two pressures balance one another and you do not feel either one.

Most of the air is close to the earth. Farther and farther away from the surface the mass of air in a unit volume decreases. In other words, the density of air decreases with altitude. For example, a cubic meter of air at sea level and a temperature of 0°C has a mass of about 1.3 kilograms (2.9 pounds). The same volume, a cubic meter, of air at about 20,000 feet and the same 0°C temperature has a mass of about 0.6 kilograms (1.3 pounds).

The decrease of density with height can be explained in terms of the number of air molecules in a unit volume. With increasing elevation the number of air molecules in a cubic meter, for example, decreases. Where does it go to zero? It is not possible to get a really satisfactory answer to that question unless you first state what you mean by "zero pressure." We do know that 99.999 per cent of the mass of air is included within an altitude of 50 miles. The atmosphere can be regarded as a thin shell surrounding the very much thicker earth.

The scarcity of gas molecules at great distances from the earth and the increase in density downward have been illustrated dramatically since the launching of the first artificial satellites. A satellite in orbit at an altitude of several hundred miles goes round and round the earth for months, or even years. The speeds of motion are in the 20,000 miles per hour class. And all this without the use of any power! Once the vehicle is kicked into orbit, it coasts at these fantastic speeds for astoundingly long periods of time.

As you may know, at the upper levels of the atmosphere, where the satellites orbit, there now are hundreds of pieces of equipment circling the globe. There are live and dead satellites, old rocket casings and miscellaneous parts, probably even some nuts and bolts. Why do they stay there? This state of affairs is no surprise to the rocketeers who put them there. According to nature's laws of motion the objects will continue on their orbital journey until their speeds are slowed down sufficiently to allow them to move toward the earth. When a satellite is in the lower atmosphere the bombardment of countless air molecules rapidly slows it down. At altitudes of several hundred miles the density of air molecules is so small that the effect of air on the satellite—we call it the *drag*—is minute, and the speed of motion remains almost constant. There is some deceleration in fact, but it is extremely small.

When the astronauts in a manned satellite want to head for home, retrorockets are fired to slow down the vehicle. The loss of speed causes the craft to move toward the earth in a great arc. As the capsule plunges through the denser atmosphere at high speeds air molecules in increasing numbers blast the forward end. It takes shields of special materials to protect the spacecraft and occupants from the searing heat. These experiences, which we all have witnessed in part on television, clearly illustrate that lowly molecules of air that cannot be seen, felt, tasted, or smelled can do a great deal of damage when the number and speeds of impact are great.

The upper layers of the earth's atmosphere have many fascinating properties. So do the rockets and satellites and the people who fly them. But they will have to be the subject of another volume. For our present purpose, we cite them only to illustrate that the mass of the air covering and bathing the earth is really fairly shallow compared to the size of the solid globe.

As we already mentioned, virtually all the air is within about 50 miles of the oceans, plains, and mountains. If all the waste particles and gases spewed into the atmosphere could be well mixed through this depth, we would not have much to worry about on the air pollution score, at least for a long stretch into the future. But it does not work that way. Only small quantities of the impurities get above 2 miles. In some cases, the smoke, gases, and fog are restricted to a depth of only several hundred feet.

The Movement of Air

When winds are strong there seldom is an air pollution problem except in sandy, desert areas. Though a city may be producing large quantities of smoke, dust, and other irritants, the wind carries them along and spreads them over a large volume of air. This spreading lowers the overall concentration. On the other hand, very light winds favor the buildup of large and dangerous concentrations of pollutants.

Winds, then, are important to know about. Have you ever wondered what makes the air move from here to there? The answer, at least in general terms, is straightforward.

When an object is at rest, it stays at rest until a force is exerted on it. This rule is part of Newton's famous First Law of Motion. It applies to everything from the tiniest particle to the largest body in the sky, from the ant to the elephant to a sleepy student who doesn't want to get up in the morning. In order to start motion, a force must be applied.

Air moves for the same reason. A force has been applied to it. As you know, air can move up or down as well as horizontally. It is common to use the word "wind" to refer only to the latter. When a meteorologist says, "An east wind is blowing," he means the air is moving horizontally *from* the east toward the west.

Vertical air motions are commonly called currents or "drafts." Pilots talk about updrafts and downdrafts. Vertical air currents are usually quite weak except in so-called convective clouds, those having the appearance of large white cauliflowers and sometimes producing thunderstorms. In such storms updrafts and downdrafts may be more than about 60 miles per hour, but in clear air and in small non-raining clouds they are usually less than 1 mile per hour.

Winds may range from a dead calm to several hundred miles per hour in a tornado. Near the ground the average wind speed is about 10 to 20 miles per hour.

To repeat, winds are produced by forces. In particular, they are produced mostly by pressure forces. We mentioned earlier that average atmospheric pressure at the earth's surface is about 14.7 pounds per square inch. When you measure the pressure with a mercury barometer the average value is found to be 29.92 inches of mercury.*

Actually, as anyone who follows the weather reports knows, atmospheric pressure varies from place to place and from time to time. For the most part the pressure changes reflect differences in the over-all density of the air above the point where the measurement is made. In general, a warm column of air is less dense and exerts a smaller pressure than a cooler and more dense column. It is the spacial variations of pressure that cause the air to move.

* Pressure can be expressed in various units. When a mercury barometer is employed, the length of the mercury column in inches or millimeters is often used. We have mentioned the units of pounds per square inch. Meteorologists commonly use the unit of millibar. You can convert pressure from one set of units to another by means of suitable factors.

Average sea level pressure = 14 lbs/in^2
= 29.92 in. of mercury
= 760 mm of mercury
= 1013 millibars

To get an idea of how it comes about, examine Figure 10 in which we illustrate a small region of the earth where the pressure decreases regularly from north to south. Following the practice used by meteorologists we have drawn *isobars,* that is, lines along which the pressure is constant. Everywhere along each line the pressure has the value indicated on the line.

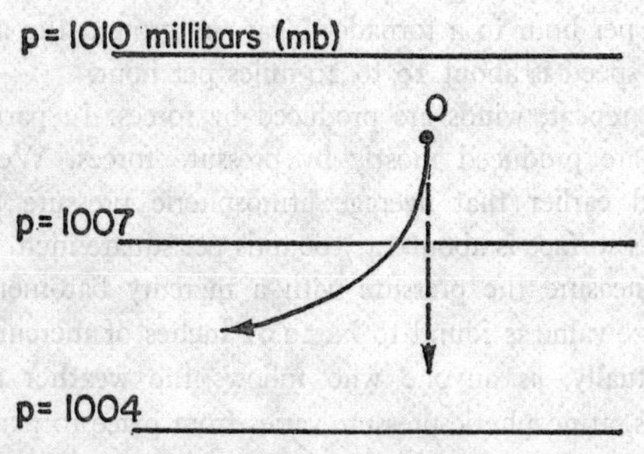

Fig. 10 The movement of a small volume of air depends on the pattern of atmospheric pressure.

Let us focus our attention on a small mass of air initially at the point marked o in Figure 10. Since the pressure to the north of it is larger than the pressure to the south, there is a force exerted on the mass of air, and this force begins to push it toward the south. If the earth were flat and stationary, the mass would move southward along the dashed arrow. But the earth is spherical and rotating, and this combination causes a deflection of the air toward the right. It is not easy to appreciate fully the explanation of this effect without considerable discussion, and for this reason we will say little about it. It has to do with the fact that as the air moves, the earth circles below it. The net effect is to cause air to be deflected toward the right of the direction of the air motion. As a result, the mass of air originally at point o moves not along the dash line, but along the solid line. You can, if you wish, consider the effects of the earth's rotation as a special kind of force acting to the right of the wind.

When you look at a weather map you often see pressure and wind patterns which have the appearance of Figure 11.

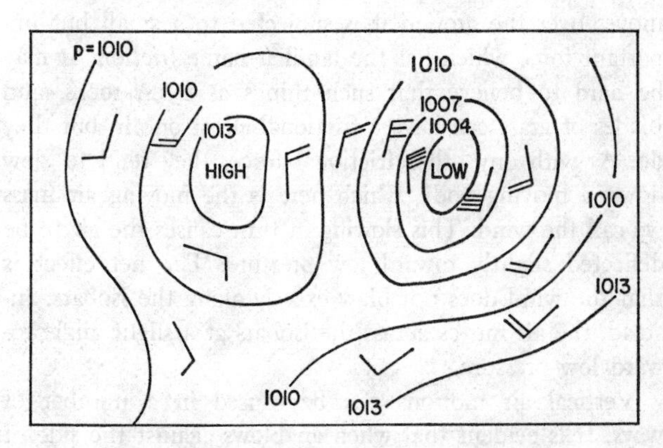

Fig. 11 Typical pressure patterns and the associated wind field.

The combined effects of the pressure force and the earth's rotation cause the winds to blow nearly parallel to the isobars. Note an important feature of this diagram. The wind direction is such that when you look downwind, low pressure is to your left. This is true in the Northern Hemisphere. As a consequence, the winds blow counterclockwise around a low pressure center and clockwise around a high pressure center. In the Southern Hemisphere, low pressure is to your right as you look downwind.

In Figure 11, the number of bars on the arrows indicates the speed; the more bars the higher the speed. As you can see, the closer the isobars the greater the speed. This result follows from the point we made earlier—namely, the winds move because of pressure forces. The closer together the isobars the greater the pressure force. In a hurricane the isobars are tightly packed and high wind speeds occur. Most often the isobars are moderately spaced and wind speeds are low.

The wind arrows in Figure 11 illustrate one more point about this subject. If you look carefully you find that the wind arrows are not quite parallel to the isobars. As the air moves over the ground it is subjected to a small but important force which has the familiar name *friction*. It may be hard to believe that such things as trees, rocks, and blades of grass can have a frictional effect on air, but they do. As with any other frictional force, they tend to slow down a moving body, which here is the moving air mass we call the wind. This slowing in turn causes the air to be deflected slightly toward low pressure. The net effect is that the wind does not blow exactly along the isobars. Instead, the air moves across the isobars at a slight angle toward low pressure.

Vertical air motions can be caused in a number of ways. It is evident that when air blows against the side of a mountain ridge, the air is forced to rise. On the other side of the mountain, sinking motion occurs. The same sort of thing happens whenever air encounters an obstacle of any size. Some vertical displacement occurs. Obviously, it depends on the size and shape of the object, the strength of the wind, and other factors as well.

Large masses of air hundreds of miles across are sometimes caused to rise when they encounter weather *fronts*. When cold, heavy air from the north moves southward and encounters warm, less dense air, the two bodies of air do not mix quickly. The cold air moves under the warm air. The boundary between the two is called a front (Figure 12a). As the cold air advances, warm air is forced to rise. If it is moist, cloud systems and rain or snow can be produced in the ascending air. When a body of warm air advances and "pushes" against a retreating body of cooler

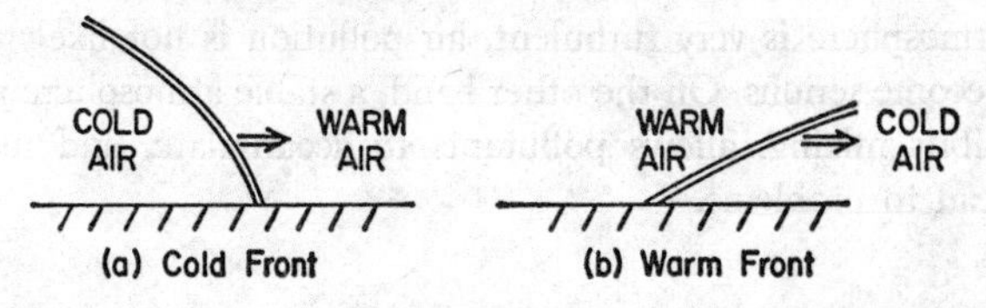

Fig. 12 Fronts separate cold-air from warm-air masses. The junction between cold-air and warm-air masses is called a front.

air, this leads to the occurrence of a "warm front" (Figure 12b). As the warm air glides up the front, extensive cloud systems with rain or snow commonly occur.

Small "bubbles" or columns of rising air can come about as a result of temperature differences. Heating of the ground by the sun's rays causes some areas to become warmer than others. When overlying masses of air become sufficiently warmer than their surroundings, they begin to rise. We say that convection takes place. It is well known that at any altitude the higher the temperature is the lower the density must be. Thus, if a mass of air is warmer than its surroundings, it is also lighter and it rises because the warmer air is subjected to an upward buoyant force.

Since water vapor is less dense than air, a humid mass of air is lighter than a dry mass of the same temperature. But the humidity effect is generally less important than the temperature effect.

Masses of air rising under the influence of temperature differences can range in size from very small volumes, which merely stir the air near the earth's surface, to regions many miles across which penetrate to the stratosphere and produce giant thunderstorms. The upward currents are counterbalanced by downward currents somewhere else. This convection leads to an overturning of the air and acts to stir up the atmosphere. Dirty air near the ground is carried up; clean air from aloft is brought down. When the atmosphere is very turbulent, air pollution is not likely to become serious. On the other hand, a stable atmosphere inhibits mixing, allows pollutants to accumulate, and may lead to problems.

Highs and Lows

Earlier, we saw how the pattern of atmospheric pressure might vary over a certain area. If you had a barograph, an instrument for recording pressure, you could see how pressure changes with time. It slowly rises, reaches a peak; then it slowly decreases, reaches a minimum, and starts to rise again. That is not to say that there is no period of constant pressure or no time when it changes abruptly. But for the most part you can regard the records as showing regions of high and low pressure moving in succession over the barograph.

The patterns of low and high pressure are quite evident when you look at a weather map. They are particularly striking on a map of a large region such as the Northern Hemisphere, shown in Figure 13. When you draw weather maps at intervals of perhaps six hours you can see how the highs and lows develop and move. Each center can be regarded as a swirling vortex imbedded in a stream of air carrying it along.

In the middle latitudes, where the belt of west winds extends up to great altitudes, you find the most rapidly changing weather events. As the highs and lows move, generally toward the east, they also change latitudes. Although there often are deviations, the low pressure centers tend to move northward as well as eastward. These centers are called *cyclones*.

Before going on, we probably should say a few words about cyclones. This term means a center of low pressure around which the air blows counterclockwise in the Northern Hemisphere and clockwise in the Southern Hemi-

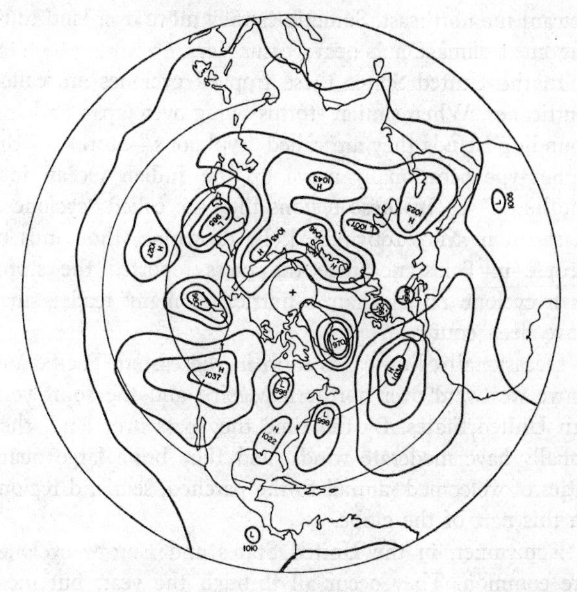

Fig. 13 Over the Northern Hemisphere at any time there are many centers of high and low pressure. The numbers near the centers of the lows and highs show the central pressure in millibars.

sphere. Among meteorologists the word cyclone is used to designate low pressure centers having diameters of several hundred to a thousand miles, with winds of light to moderate intensity around them. Sometimes, especially in the news reports, the word cyclone is used to describe tornadoes and waterspouts. These storms do have low pressures at their centers, but they are almost always less than a mile in diameter, have durations measured in minutes, and usually produce violent winds.

Hurricanes are cyclones of tropical origin. In the Northern Hemisphere they usually form over the warm oceans in the western Atlantic or Pacific Oceans. They generally move westward, then northward, and then curve toward the northeast. Sometimes they move over land causing great damage and heavy casualties.

In the United States these tropical cyclones are called hurricanes. When similar storms swing over Japan and surrounding islands they are called "typhoons." Storms of the same type occasionally move up the Indian Ocean into southern Asia. In these regions they are called "cyclones." A storm in May 1965 killed, by drowning, thousands of people in Pakistan. Since the press reported the storm as a cyclone rather than a hurricane, many readers may have been confused.

Occasionally, hurricanes form in the eastern Pacific and move westward over northern Mexico and the southwestern United States. By the time they pass over land, they usually have moderate winds, and they bring large quantities of welcomed rainfall to the parched, semiarid regions in this part of the globe.

Remember, in the United States and Europe cyclones are common. They occur all through the year, but most often in the winter. Hurricanes are infrequent and occur almost exclusively between August and October. Hurricanes are to be respected, and treated with care; cyclones usually do more good than harm. They bring rain and snow without the punishing wind, waves, and floods of the ocean-born hurricanes.

Cyclones are characterized as regions where the air rises slowly but for a long time—for periods of days. Clouds and precipitation are common. These conditions lead to what is sometimes called "bad weather," but not from the air pollution point of view. The rising air motion acts to distribute contaminants through a deep layer. Rain and snow wash out the atmosphere and carry particulates and gases to the ground.

The regions of high pressure—the anticyclones—are the troublemakers. They bring fair weather, that is, periods without rain or snow; in fact, anticyclones commonly are characterized by skies with few or no clouds. The small amount of cloudiness is understandable. Anticyclones are generally regions where the air is sinking or *subsiding,* according to a term used by meteorologists. As the air moves to lower altitudes and higher pressure, it is compressed and its temperature rises. This is illustrated in Figure 14. The subsidence usually does not go all the way to the ground. As a result of the warming aloft, inversions can be produced. They act to stabilize the atmosphere and restrict mixing to the lowest layers.

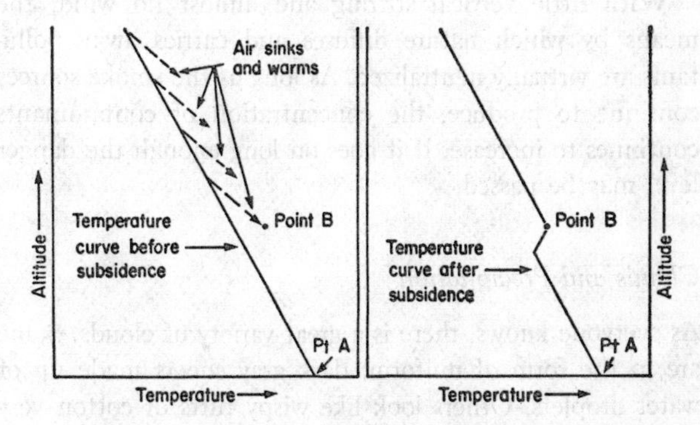

Fig. 14 The sinking of air leads to warming aloft and the formation of inversions.

The clear skies commonly associated with anticyclones also are important in allowing inversions to form close to the earth's surface. When the air is clear and dry aloft, heat may be radiated rapidly from the ground. The low-lying layers of air cool off quickly after sundown. A shallow inversion may form and trap pollution in the lowest few hundred feet of the atmosphere. Figure 2 illustrated such a low-level inversion.

Thus we see that in an anticyclone there may be a subsidence inversion aloft at perhaps several thousand feet of altitude. At night, a second inversion may form right at the surface. These stable layers act to reduce the turbulence and mixing in the atmosphere. The comparative calm allows contaminants to accumulate in a thin layer of air near the ground.

There is still another property of anticyclones contributing to the concentration of pollutants. The wind speeds around anticyclones generally are lower than those in cyclones. In some large but slow-moving high pressure systems, the winds may drop almost to a dead calm. These are the conditions that occurred in London and in Donora.

With little vertical stirring and almost no wind, the means by which nature diffuses and carries away pollutants are virtually neutralized. As long as the smoke sources continue to produce, the concentration of contaminants continues to increase. If it goes on long enough the danger level may be passed.

Clouds and Precipitation

As everyone knows, there is a great variety of clouds. Some are in the form of uniform, dark gray sheets made up of water droplets. Others look like wispy tufts of cotton very high in the sky. These clouds are composed of ice crystals and are called "cirrus." The brilliant white cauliflower-shaped clouds most common in the summer are called "cumulus."

With the exception of fog, almost all clouds are produced as a result of the ascent of air. When air rises to higher altitudes, it expands and its temperature decreases. At the same time its relative humidity increases. When the relative humidity approaches 100 per cent, water molecules condense on particles in the air. The fantastic number of tiny water droplets produced constitute the cloud. If air temperatures are far below freezing, ice crystals may be produced directly, instead of water droplets. However, it is an interesting and important fact that in the atmosphere, water-droplet clouds often form and persist when temperatures are as low as −10°C or even lower.

It is clear that clouds come into being because of condensation. But it is not so clear that rain and snow generally will *not* form as a result of condensation alone. Some people have the idea that a raindrop is merely a result of continued condensation until a drop is large enough to fall to the ground. This is not the case except, possibly, in certain dense fogs especially near the sea. In such case, you sometimes get drizzle.

In a cloud there are many droplets, about a hundred or so per cubic centimeter. When the available moisture is shared among them by condensation none can grow large enough to become raindrops. In general, the smaller ones grow faster than the larger ones. For rain or snow to form it is necessary for something besides the usual condensation process to come into play. The details of the known precipitation mechanisms have been discussed elsewhere.† At this point, it should be adequate to mention briefly their chief characteristics. We know of two precipitation formation processes. One is called the "coalescence process." In order for it to proceed, condensation must lead to some droplets about five times larger than the average droplet diameters. In such a circumstance, the larger drops can fall through the cloud of smaller ones. This movement leads to the collision and coalescence of the droplets. The larger drops grow, fall faster, grow larger, etc. If the cloud is deep enough, rain is produced.

We mentioned that clouds of water droplets having temperatures below −10°C or so are fairly common in the atmosphere. We say such clouds are *supercooled*. As long as ice crystals are not present, a supercooled cloud may be stable and last for hours without producing pre-

†See L. J. Battan, *Cloud Physics and Cloud Seeding*, Science Study Series. Doubleday Anchor (1962).

cipitation. On the other hand, when some ice crystals are introduced, usually because a special type of solid particle enters the cloud, the behavior of the cloud may change rapidly. As few as one ice crystal for every million cloud droplets can have a profound effect. The ice crystals can grow rapidly by the direct deposition of water molecules on the ice. As the crystals grow, the water droplets evaporate.

When the ice crystals are large enough to fall through the supercooled cloud, they can grow even faster by colliding with the droplets and other crystals. In this way snowflakes or ice pellets or hail may be produced. On a winter day with subfreezing temperature, the ice crystals and snowflakes reach the ground. Blankets of white may cloak the countryside. Drifts may cover the driveways and clog the highways if the cloud system is deep and widespread.

On other days, the temperature near the ground may be above freezing. In such a circumstance, the falling ice particles can melt on their way down and reach the surface as rain. In mountainous areas it is common in the winter to have rain in valleys while layers of snow top the surrounding summits.

Precipitation of any form is extremely important in considering the history of pollutants in the atmosphere. In particular, rain washes particles out of the air. Collisions of raindrops and aerosols may leave the particles deposited on the drops. The effectiveness of this process depends on the size of the raindrops and of the particles. With the usual types of rain, particles smaller than a few microns are not swept out very efficiently. Instead of colliding with a raindrop, most aerosols with diameters below about 4 microns stay in the airstream flowing around the drop.

As particle diameters increase, the collection by raindrops becomes more efficient. It has been estimated that in about an hour, even a light rain can wash out half the particles 10 microns or greater.

Rainfall cleans out the atmosphere in another way besides the one just described. We mentioned earlier that cloud droplets form by condensation on small particles. The radii of most range from about 0.1 to 1.0 microns. Sea salt particles are efficient condensation nuclei. Most of the smaller nuclei are thought to be sulfate-bearing particles, such as the ones produced by air pollution sources. Certain nitrate particles also may serve as the nuclei. The resulting cloud droplets combine with raindrops as a result of the collision and coalescence. When they fall to the ground, they carry sulfates and nitrates with them. Incidentally, these two substances add nutrients to the soil and make it more fertile.

The chief mechanisms by which aerosols are removed from the atmosphere are (1) direct fallout, either by sedimentation or impaction on the surface, and (2) washout. Close to the source of the pollutants, near a smokestack for example, fallout is most important, but there is evidence to indicate that beyond a few miles from the source, washout by precipitation becomes more significant in the long run. One of the important features of washout is that it works through a deep layer of the atmosphere. Thunderstorms with precipitation columns extending even into the stratosphere can bring down particles from great altitudes.

in [illegible] light [illegible] can wash out [illegible] the [illegible] greater.

[illegible] may be [illegible] covered [illegible] gathered [illegible] that [illegible] droplets form by condensation on small particles. Their diameters range from about 0.1 to [illegible] particles [illegible] condensation [illegible] greater nuclei are thought to be [illegible] particles. [illegible] Certain [illegible] the resulting [illegible] droplets [illegible] as a result of collision [illegible] When they fall to the ground, they are [illegible] with [illegible] these [illegible] to the soil and make it more fertile.

The chief mechanisms by which aerosols are removed from the atmosphere are (1) [illegible] out [illegible] particles [illegible] (2) washout [illegible] the [illegible] for example [illegible] important [illegible] many miles from the [illegible] more significant [illegible] atmosphere [illegible] that [illegible] the atmosphere. Thunderstorms with [illegible] into [illegible] from great distances.

Chapter VIII

THE ATMOSPHERE AS A DUMPING GROUND

We have discussed, in earlier chapters, the depth and mass of the atmosphere. The numbers are impressive, particularly when we remember that by far the greater part of our lives is lived in a thin layer, rising not much more than a hundred feet above the ground.

With some exceptions, sources of pollution are also down in our layer of air. Certainly, those prolific sources, the automobile, the bus, and the truck, are close to the ground. Most tailpipes are below the three-foot level. The important sources extending above man's level are smokestacks, but in certain circumstances even a tall stack is of little value in keeping smoke from reaching the ground.

Whenever a question is raised about the seriousness of a source of air pollution several factors have to be considered. How much of which substances in what form is being released? Where is it being released with respect to human, animal, or plant communities? When are the pollutants being released and under what meteorological conditions?

The atmosphere is often treated as a garbage pail of infinite size. Obviously, this is a serious mistake. Our layer of air should not be regarded as a dumping ground in any circumstance. The quantity of pollutants that can safely be put into the air depends on the properties of the atmosphere at the moment of release and subsequently. In some periods a great deal of smoke can be added with little danger. At other times the addition of contaminants must be kept at an absolute minimum. To ascertain whether or not it is safe to release large quantities of pollutants, it is necessary to consider those properties of the atmosphere that determine over how large a region—in depth, breadth, and length—the pollutants will be spread.

Diffusion

Meteorologists concerned with the spread of any property through the atmosphere give a great deal of thought to a process called *diffusion*. In general, the term means the spreading out of that property. Usually, we mean the spreading produced by the smaller-scale air motions rather than the large, steady wind currents.

Have you ever seen a small rocket fired into the air at a Fourth of July fireworks display? When it reaches an altitude of a few hundred feet, the head of the rocket explodes. It throws out a shower of colored lights. It also produces a puff of smoke. If you watch the smoke, you will notice several features of its movement. First, under the influence of the wind, the entire puff moves as a single unit. In addition, the size of the smoke region increases (Figure 15). This spreading comes about as a result of variations of small-scale air motions. They move the smoke particles farther away from the center of the puff. We say that they cause the smoke to diffuse outward.

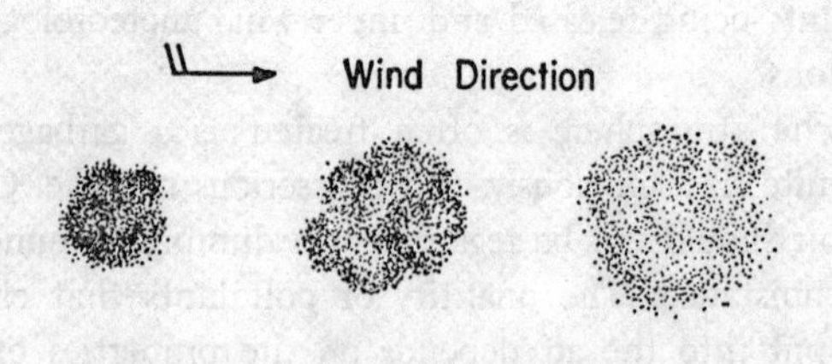

Fig. 15 A puff of smoke diffuses outward at the same time as it moves with the wind.

When you examine the motions in the smoke puff, you find that not all the air movement is outward. In some places the motion is outward, while in others it is inward. The air motion is turbulent. The net result of the turbulent motion, in a region of differing smoke concentration, is to transport smoke from the region of high to the region of low concentration.

In its most general sense, diffusion acts in a variety of ways. For example, it happens on a molecular scale. When a drop of water is suspended on a thread in a jar containing *still* air with a relative humidity of 50 per cent, the drop slowly evaporates. For this to happen the water molecules must leave the water and be transported away from the air layer immediately over the drop. Right at the surface of the drop the relative humidity can be regarded as being 100 per cent; away from the drop it is 50 per cent. The concentration of water vapor molecules in the air decreases sharply with distance away from the drop. All the molecules are in constant movement. The number of water molecules moving away from the drop is greater than the number moving toward the drop. This process is called *molecular diffusion.*

Molecular diffusion occurs in the free atmosphere too. It acts to spread heat from warm to cool air, water vapor from moist to dry air; but molecular diffusion is of negligible importance when compared with what is called *eddy diffusion,* which is caused by turbulent air motions. The chief difference is that an average air molecule near the ground travels only 0.00001 cm before colliding with another molecule. Turbulent motions, on the other hand, extend over distances measured in terms of centimeters to hundreds of meters.

In thinking of eddy diffusion, imagine the air made up of swirling eddies. Each one can be thought of as a sphere of swirling air. In the puff of smoke from our skyrocket the eddies might have diameters of several centimeters to several meters. In a layer of smoke air near the ground, eddies up to several kilometers in diameter are important. As the eddies move, they transport smoke from places of high to places of low concentration. It is important to recognize that the eddies vary in size and number. The contribution of each size in causing diffusion depends also on the size of the smoke puff. In general, the smaller the puff, the smaller the eddies causing diffusion. The very large eddies can carry along the entire puff without causing it to spread.

The rate at which diffusion transports any substance depends upon factors besides the size of the eddies. As you might expect, the greater the concentration of pollutants at one place with respect to the surroundings, the more rapid the spread. To use the specific term employed by the experts, we say that as the *gradient* of concentration increases, the rate of transport increases. The gradient is obtained by measuring the concentration at two points and dividing by the distance between the two points.

What are the properties of the atmosphere producing eddy motions? The wind leads to what is sometimes called *mechanical turbulence*. The moving air strikes obstructions such as rocks, trees, buildings, etc., and is caused to move up and down, side to side, slow down and speed up. Also, when the wind velocity changes rapidly over small distances, even in the free atmosphere, turbulent motions are produced.

Stability of the Atmosphere

But important as the wind is in causing diffusion, a second property of the atmosphere is even more important. We have referred to this property several times in speaking of the *stability* of the air. In particular, this term is used as a measure of the thermal properties of the atmosphere.

Let us consider what is meant by stability. A large rock delicately balanced on the side of a cliff can be said to be potentially unstable. As long as it is not pushed, it might remain there for years. On the other hand, if you gave it a little push, it would go over the cliff and fall until it crashed into the valley below. We say that the instability was realized because, once a small displacement was produced, it was followed by an ever-increasing displacement.

Consider another example. Put a small balloon in a tub of water. Obviously, it floats. If you forced the balloon under water and released it, what would happen? Again, obviously, it would return to the surface. In this case, we have a stable system. A small displacement was not followed by a larger one but rather was followed by a return of the balloon to its original position.

It is well known that the atmosphere is sometimes stable, sometimes unstable, and sometimes neither. In this last case, it is called *neutral*. In a stable atmosphere a volume of air displaced from its original altitude tends to return to that altitude. The initial displacement could come about because of the mechanical turbulence referred to earlier.

In an unstable atmosphere, a mass of air given a small displacement does not return to its original altitude. Instead, it accelerates in the direction of the displacement, either up or down.

As you probably have surmised by now, in a neutral atmosphere a displaced mass of air remains at the altitude to which it moved. It neither accelerates in the original direction nor returns to the original altitude.

Whether or not the air is stable, unstable, or neutral depends on the temperature variations in the atmosphere in relation to the temperature of a displaced volume of air. Let us call it a "parcel" of air. Imagine, for example, that as the wind blew over a rocky field, a small parcel—perhaps a cubic meter—of air was caused to rise 100 meters above its original altitude. If by the time the parcel got there it was warmer than the surrounding air, then it would be less dense and would continue accelerating upward. The atmosphere in this case would be unstable. If by contrast when the small volume of air reached the 100-meter level it was colder and more dense than the environment, it would sink back toward the ground. This represents stability. Finally, if the small parcel of air on reaching 100 meters found itself with the same temperature and same density as the environment, it would remain there. We would say the atmosphere was neutral. The stability of the atmosphere, therefore, depends on the temperature of a displaced volume of air relative to the environment at the same altitude.

The next question to be answered is what property of the atmosphere governs the relative temperature? The answer is simply the rate at which the temperature *decreases* with altitude. This quantity is called the *temperature lapse rate.* When the temperature at the ground is 31.2°C and the temperature at an altitude of 200 meters is 30.0°C, the lapse rate is $\frac{31.2 - 30.0°\text{C}}{200 \text{ meters}}$ or 0.6°C/100 meters.

The lapse rate in the atmosphere may vary over a wide range. It averages about 0.6°C/100 m (about 3.6°F/1000 ft.). But close to the ground in a hot, dry desert it can exceed 20°C/100 m (about 110°F/1000 ft.). When there is an inversion, the temperature increases with height, and the lapse rate has a negative sign. It might be, for example, –0.6°C/100 m. If the temperature is constant with height, the lapse rate equals zero and the atmosphere is said to be "isothermal."

In considering stability we commonly assume that the environment is at rest and that the temperature at any altitude varies slowly. On the contrary, the temperature of ascending or descending parcels of air may change rapidly.

Consider again a small volume of air rising from the surface at a speed of 1 meter/second. In about a minute and a half it would reach an altitude of about 100 meters. Assume also that no heat is added or taken away by such processes as radiation or conduction. If there were a thermometer in the parcel you would find that by the time it reached that altitude its temperature would have fallen 1°C. Why?

As the volume ascended it moved toward lower pressure. As a result it expanded. The same thing happens to balloons when they rise to higher altitudes and lower pressures. The gas molecules inside the balloon force the rubber outward until the pressure inside and outside are the same. As a result the balloon expands. In expanding, the rising volume of air gives up some of its energy. Scientists say the expanding air does *work* on the surroundings. As a result, the air parcel decreases in temperature. This is an interesting fact as you think about it. The temperature of the rising air decreases even though no heat is taken away. Energy is lost but no heat is lost. This seems like a paradox. But note that heat is only one form of energy. A discussion of this point would take us off the main track here. The important point to remember is that expansion leads to cooling. Conversely, compression leads to warming.

The rate of temperature change of a volume of dry air being displaced vertically is constant and equal to 1°C/100 meters. Meteorologists call this the *dry adiabatic lapse rate*. The word adiabatic denotes that no heat is added or taken away from the parcel. The adjective dry designates a process in which neither condensation nor evaporation occurs. When either of them occurs in a displaced parcel of air, the term *moist adiabatic lapse rate* is employed. This rate is smaller than 1°C/100 m and varies with temperature and altitude. However, for most air pollution studies we can restrict the discussion to the dry case.

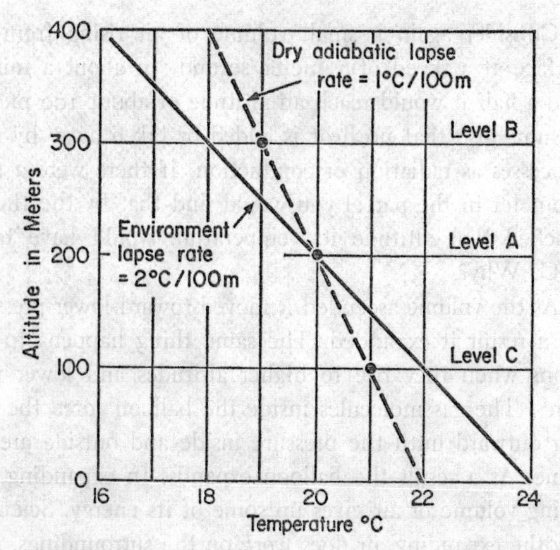

Fig. 16 When the environment lapse rate is greater than the dry adiabatic lapse rate, the atmosphere is unstable.

Let us return now to a consideration of stability. Figure 16 illustrates the temperature structure on a day when the air is unstable. The lapse rate is 2°C/100 m. Consider the air originally at altitude A. If for some reason it were displaced to altitude B, it would follow the dashed line representing the dry adiabatic lapse rate. In other words, it would cool off at the rate of 1°C/100 m. When it reached B, the parcel would find itself warmer and less dense than the environment and continue rising. If the parcel were moved to level C, it would be cooler and more dense than the environment and continue to descend.

Figure 17 shows what happens in the case of an inversion. Again the rising parcel of air moves dry adiabatically. However, in this case when it reaches level B it finds itself colder and more dense than the environment. It sinks back toward level A along the dry adiabat. If the parcel were

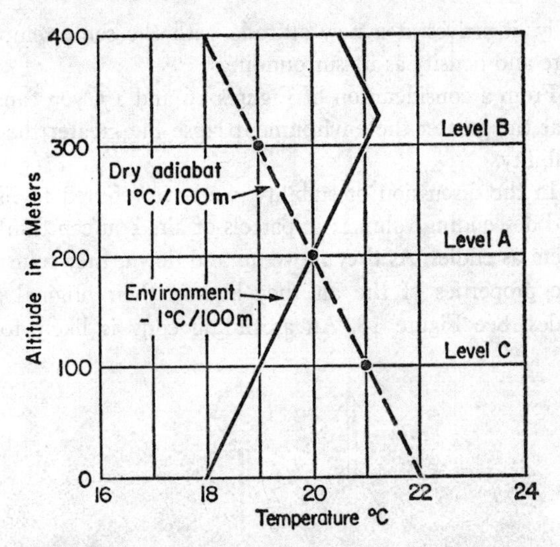

Fig. 17 *When the environment lapse rate is smaller than the dry adiabatic lapse rate, the atmosphere is stable.*

displaced to level C it would become warmer and less dense than its surroundings. It would become buoyant and return to level A. This illustration shows why inversions produce stability and suppress mixing.

As already mentioned, lapse rates in the atmosphere extend over a large range. For this reason, stabilities also vary greatly. Diagrams such as those shown in Figures 16 and 17 can be used to determine whether or not the atmosphere is stable or unstable, and the degree of either condition. You can see that the boundary line between stability and unstability is the dry adiabatic lapse rate. When the environment lapse rate is greater than the adiabatic the atmosphere is unstable. When the environment lapse rate is smaller the atmosphere is stable. When the environment lapse rate is exactly equal to the adiabatic lapse rate the atmosphere is neutral. If the air is displaced vertically, it arrives at a new altitude with the same temperature and density as its surroundings.

From a consideration of Figures 16 and 17, you can see that the greater the environment lapse the greater the unstability.

In the discussion of stability, we have referred to rising and descending volumes or parcels of air. You can think of them as eddies. As they move up and down, they transport the properties of the air they had at their original altitudes. See Figure 18. An ascending eddy is likely to be

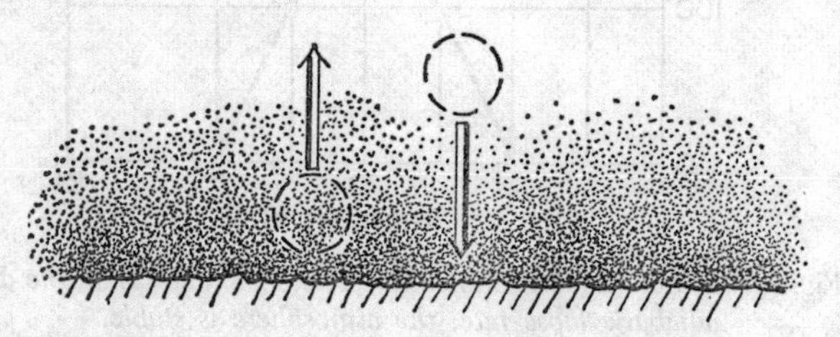

Fig. 18 Upward- and downward-moving eddies act to transport and diffuse pollutants through a greater depth of the atmosphere.

transporting more polluted air than a descending eddy. The latter is likely to be carrying cleaner air downward.

Clearly, the most favorable times for releasing pollutants into the atmosphere from the ground are those with large lapse rates. When the air is stable, and particularly when there is a strong inversion, pollution sources should be shut down as much as possible.

Stack Meteorology

Most often we think of eddy diffusion as an agency for transporting pollutants upward from the ground, but this is not always the case. Sometimes, when smokestacks are the sources, diffusion transports the effluents downward.

Because of the fact that smokestacks are used so often for the disposal of noxious gases and aerosols, there has been a great deal of study of how the stacks function under various meteorological conditions. One of the chief aims has been the accumulation of the knowledge needed to properly design and build stacks.

The behavior of a plume of smoke coming out of a high chimney depends mostly on the strength of the wind and the stability of the atmosphere. On the basis of investigations of a great many smoke plumes, scientists have adopted a scheme for classifying them. Three common classes of plumes are illustrated in Figure 19.

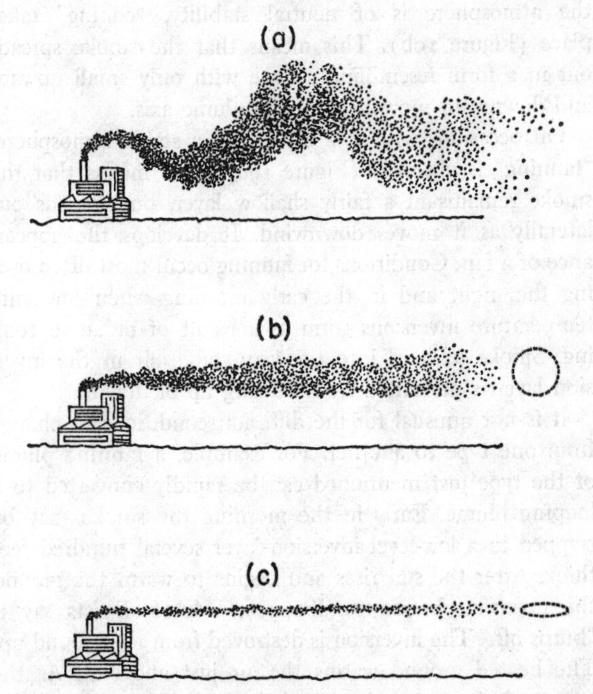

Fig. 19 The character of a smoke plume depends on the stability of the atmosphere and the wind velocity.

When the wind is light to moderate but the air is unstable, a "looping" plume occurs (Figure 19a). It is characterized by a very wavy appearance. Sometimes parts of the plume brush the ground close to the stack. The second feature of a looping plume is that diffusion causes it to spread out rapidly. This result follows from the fact that when the air is unstable, diffusion is great.

Earlier we mentioned that when polluted air is close to the ground, large temperature lapse rates lead to a rapid upward diffusion. As can be seen, under the same conditions a smoke layer aloft can be diffused downward rapidly.

When the winds are greater than about 20 m.p.h., and the atmosphere is of neutral stability, "coning" takes place (Figure 19b). This means that the smoke spreads out in a form resembling a cone with only small upward and downward movement of the plume axis.

On occasions with low winds and a stable atmosphere, "fanning" is observed (Figure 19c). This means that the smoke remains in a fairly shallow layer, but spreads out laterally as it moves downwind. It develops the appearance of a fan. Conditions for fanning occur most often during the night and in the early morning when low-lying temperature inversions form as a result of radiative cooling. Smoke released into the very stable air in the inversion layer is prevented from moving up or down.

It is not unusual for the diffusion conditions to change from one type to another. For example, a fanning plume of the type just mentioned can be rapidly converted to a looping plume. Early in the morning the smoke may be trapped in a low-level inversion layer several hundred feet thick. After the sun rises and begins to warm the ground the inversion begins to disappear. Meteorologists say it "burns off." The inversion is destroyed from the ground up. The heated ground warms the air just above it. As the lowest air is heated, it rises and mixes through a deeper and deeper layer. When the depth of the mixing layer reaches the level of the smoke plume, there is a rapid downward spread of the smoke. This result is sometimes called "fumigation."

In the design of a smokestack it is crucial to know how high to make it in order to minimize the quantities of smoke reaching the ground. As you would expect, the higher the stack, the smaller the concentration of smoke at the ground. In general, as the stack height increases the concentration decreases as the square of the height. Thus if the height is double, the concentration is reduced by ($\frac{1}{2} \times \frac{1}{2}$), or one-quarter.

It is also important to know where the smoke reaches the ground. It has been found that the higher the stack, the greater the distance downwind infected by smoke pollutants.

Of course, there are exceptions to these two general rules. In cases of extreme looping, smoke from even the highest stack might reach the ground in very high concentration. Furthermore, the concentration might occur very close to the stack. On the other hand, with a strong inversion it is possible that almost no smoke will be carried down to the ground from even short stacks.

How well you can predict what a smoke plume will do depends largely on how well the weather conditions can be predicted. This in turn depends on the climate of the region in question. For these reasons meteorologists and climatologists have had an important part in studies of air pollution.

In this section, we have merely sketched some of the factors which should be considered when putting up a smokestack. The problems involved have been oversimplified. The object of this brief discussion has not been to cover the problem in detail, but rather to emphasize the importance of taking atmospheric conditions into account in designing a smokestack. It is equally important to consider them in determining when it is safe and when it is not safe to release large quantities of smoke.

Point, Line, and Area Sources

It is most easy to visualize what happens to pollutants when you consider a puff of smoke or a steady stream coming out of a smokestack. However, it should be recognized that most often, the serious problems arise when there are many sources rather than just one. A single smokestack is often regarded as a *point source* because of its small size. When there is a line of them close together, it is more appropriate to think of them as a *line source*. Specifically, they would represent an elevated line source. A busy highway in the open country can be thought of as a line source at the ground because the vehicles will be producing pollutants along a line.

Finally, a city can be considered as an *area source*. Within it there would be smokestacks and chimneys, cars and trucks, and people too, all contributing to the production of air pollution.

Line sources and area sources have not received as much scientific attention as have point sources. One of the reasons for this state of affairs is the fact that the point sources are easier to investigate. From the practical view, the point source probably is the least important except in instances of industrial disaster, for example, an explosion in a nuclear power plant. It is anticipated that the growing concern with air pollution will lead to more study of contaminants released from line and area sources.

Chapter IX

PATHS TO IMPROVEMENT

Almost everyone agrees that something must be done about air pollution. Politicians, newspapermen, scientists, industrialists, doctors, they all tell us the situation is getting worse. The air is becoming a vast sewer with poisonous gases and aerosols accumulating at a disturbing rate.

Where the terrain is flat and the winds are commonly strong, the pollutants are quickly blown away and may not pose a serious threat to beauty, health, or long life. But over too many cities the atmosphere forms a reservoir for the collection of incredibly large quantities of muck.

But what can be done about it? We know that polluted air is part of the price of progress. The Industrial Revolution was a great step toward a better life for more people. It brought about giant manufacturing complexes producing astonishing quantities of steel, chemicals, and thousands of other goods. People migrated to cities to find jobs in the new industries. Houses, schools, theaters were built. The cities became larger and larger. Some of them have swelled so much they have merged in geography if not in government.

All these changes have contributed to polluting the air. Most fabricating processes produce smoke. Power plants burning fossil fuels do likewise. Coal and oil furnaces in houses are smoke generators. In rural areas, with widely separated houses, these domestic sources of pollution do not add up to much. But in cities, with their tightly packed buildings, the contributions of a great many chimneys multiply the problems.

If you were to start from a barren piece of ground and design a city, you could spare the future residents some of the grief so many of us suffer now. You could zone the city to situate the most serious smoke producers on the side that would be leeward of the community in those periods when the air was most often stable and the winds light. You could enact local laws governing how and when smoke could be released.

A good planner would make use of parks to separate the residences from the industries to allow for a buffer zone between the most serious smoke producers and most of the people. Still another ordinance would insist that gas or electricity be used for fuel, instead of coal and oil.

Finally and possibly most importantly, you would do some thinking about transportation.

Little could Henry Ford have imagined, when he built his car and showed the world that the horse's days were numbered, what would be the consequences of his conception. He and his successors probably foresaw, at least in vague terms, that one day the automobile would replace the carriage and that trucks would supplant the wagon. But how could anyone have imagined that this magnificent machine could turn out to have so many faults?

Now there will be many who still see only the good and not the evil in a sleek machine with polished chrome and several hundred horses under the hood. But let us remember for a minute that in 1965 more than 49,000 Americans went to their graves as a direct result of the automobile. That represents a great many people—more than one hundred per day. And as the number of machines increases, the number of fatalities does too. From some points of view the automobile is becoming one of modern society's chief social diseases.

The crunching and grinding of steel and glass when two

cars try at high speed to occupy the same part of the road is the obvious and immediately frightening evidence of one of the evils of automobiles. But the one we are concerned with in this book is much less obvious; it is the one done slowly, quietly, and continuously. The gases and particles flowing out of every tail pipe are slowly but surely contributing to the buildup of toxic substances in the air. We have already discussed the insidious effects of the hydrocarbons, the sulfur and nitrogen oxides, and carbon monoxide on the life and death of plants and animals. We saw how even the stones of which statues and buildings are made suffer from some of these substances.

But again, what's to be done about it?

Industrial Smokes

In the early days, some decades ago, when public-spirited citizens began to agitate for smoke control, they were seldom heard, often ignored, and sometimes ridiculed by those who were in positions to do something about it. The city of Pittsburgh was a good example. It was warmly and rightly called "The Smoky City" by those who did not have to live there. One drive through it was enough to convince most people. It was not a nice place to live, and not even a good place to visit. What beauty is there in walls darkened beyond recognition, street signs so black they could not be read? In one month the quantity of particles falling out of the air reached the staggering total of 291 tons per square mile. There may be some people who enjoy the smell of smoke, but they are not many.

The downtown area of Pittsburgh, particularly, was plagued with the smoke from steel mills and coal-burning locomotives. Before 1943, local groups in and out of the city government tried to do something to reduce the problems of smoke contamination and the decay of the city. Plans for control were met with threats by some steel producers to move out of the city. Confronted with economic blackmail, local authorities found it impossible to make much progress.

But then some powerful banking and industrial interests brushed their own dust from their eyes and looked into the future. It was clear that Pittsburgh was going downhill and gears had to be shifted. A conference of interested parties was organized to face the problems of city planning from all points of view. In 1945, a long-range plan for developing the real estate and cleansing the air above it was formulated. This advance was followed up with effective implementation of urban renewal and smoke abatement provisions.

An almost miraculous change was brought about in Pittsburgh. In a matter of four years it was transformed from a dramatic example of how bad a city can get with too little planning and too much smoke, to a city that is the pride of its residents and the whole state. It is taller, cleaner, and has a shinier future. Industry has profited, the people have profited, and the country has too.

There was an important lesson to be learned from the scrubbing up of The Smoky City. It showed that even the most industrialized community can be changed, and in short order. But it is necessary, first, for the leading citizens to understand the problems and to want to change them. To work in the direction of city planning and air pollution control is to "cast bread upon the water"—or perhaps to waft a fragrance to the sky. The efforts lead to great rewards to all who live in and breathe the air surrounding them.

It is not our intention to discuss means for cleaning the air from industrial smokestacks. There are books on the subject for those who want to know. Engineers know how to do it. They have devices for capturing particles before they can leave the stack. In some cases, the particles form a valuable by-product which can be sold. Certain types of fly ash are used in some grades of cement, for example.

Some gases that used to be exhausted to the air can be captured and condensed or absorbed and then extracted and used for other industrial purposes. For example, sulfur dioxide can be recovered and converted to usable form.

Often the leaders of industry do not readily see the overall advantages in taking those steps needed to reduce the quantity of pollutants their plants contribute to the atmosphere. Sometimes, costly equipment is needed. Expensive studies are required to ascertain the best course of action. Notwithstanding these factors, it is vital to examine the experiences of those communities where the costs have been met and effective steps taken to clean the air, or at least to try to keep it from getting any dirtier. In so doing, all the citizens have profited, some in ways which may never be known. A man may never thank a steel mill executive because a reduction in pollutants by that plant prevented him from developing emphysema. He may not know it himself. On the other hand, a decrease in absenteeism because of healthier employees will be reflected in a more profitable operation.

In the thirties and forties it was a common practice to burn trash in small incinerators or baskets in the back yard. A small number would be of little concern, of course, but when thousands of these inefficient disposal units go on at the same time, they contribute to the pollution over a city. Fortunately, most larger cities have adopted ordinances prohibiting local burning of trash. This restriction leads to cleaner air; it also cuts down on the number of brush fires, fence and house fires.

Meteorologists Can Help

So far we have been discussing the need to reduce the quantities of impurities put into the air. Unless the input of pollutants is reduced, other steps for reducing the problems will be of limited value. Fortunately, at all levels of government, particularly in Washington, there is a growing awareness of the seriousness of the situation, and means are being explored for reducing the hazards.

The seriousness of air pollution, as we noted earlier, depends on the amounts of gases and particles in relation to the amounts of air into which they are dumped. The unpleasantness or danger of a particular pollutant depends on the concentration. The concentration can be reduced in two ways. The quantity of pollutant can be reduced, or the quantity of air increased. The first is simpler, and in the long run more essential, because the atmosphere is limited in size and cannot be expanded.

On a local scale, however, an understanding of the atmosphere can be crucial in the air pollution war. We saw earlier that the most serious problems arise when there is a strong, low-level temperature inversion with light winds. In this condition the gases and smokes are trapped in a small space. The concentrations increase as time goes on. On the other hand, when the atmosphere is unstable and the winds are strong, the pollutants are distributed over a large body of air.

These facts form the basis for rules on when to restrict and when to allow smoke and other pollutants to be released into the atmosphere. During the stable periods only essential burning should be permitted. Most incineration should be done on days with unstable and turbulent air. Meteorologists can predict, with some degree of reliability, the conditions to be expected one to two days in advance. This information should be used by air pollution control agencies in planning their moves.

The meteorologist also can supply important climatological information. In city planning it is essential that the smoke producers be placed downwind from the residential area. Local topographic features make some places better than others for locating a pollution source. In certain valleys there are often light winds tending to blow up the valley in the daytime and down the valley at night. A large smoke generator in the wrong place can keep such a city under a slowly oscillating pall of smoke.

If you have industry, you have some smoke. It has been traditional to use smokestacks to try to reduce the deleterious effects. Various factors must be taken into account when designing the stacks. The properties of the effluent are important. For example, is the gas heavier or lighter than air? The climatology of the area also must be taken into account because the behavior of the gases and particles after they enter the atmosphere depends, in an important way, on the properties of the atmosphere. In one area very tall stacks may be absolutely necessary; in another relatively short ones may be adequate.

In summary, the meteorologist can supply information which should be used in locating and designing smoke-producing structures. He can and should be called in for interpretation of climatological information. Meteorologists also can describe and predict those weather situations when the concentration of pollutants can reach unpleasant or toxic levels. This information can be used to issue warnings and to initiate control measures to reduce the addition of gases and particles when atmospheric conditions are unfavorable.

Automobiles and Other Vehicles

We mentioned earlier that Pittsburgh has leaped upward along the scale of cleanliness. Other cities have also made great strides in this direction. But none have really whipped the problem of air pollution. The reason lies in the ever-increasing numbers of motor cars.

As prosperity has expanded and ever-increasing numbers of people have shared in the benefits, the number of automobiles has increased tremendously. During 1965, over nine million new automobiles were sold in the United States. An equal or greater number is expected to be produced for some time in the future, unless there is a drastic reversal in the economic health of the country.

In addition to greater numbers, there is also an increase in power. The craving for the small car which swept the country during the early 1960's has largely abated, and the big car with the big engine is back. The question of what should be done about the exhausts of automobiles remains, and the answer is not as obvious as it may seem. For years, California lawmakers have been urging the development and installation of devices to reduce the quantity of pollutants automobiles emit. Various devices have been developed by the auto manufacturers and are to be installed on all new cars, starting in 1966. These gadgets are designed primarily to cut the quantity of carbon monoxide and hydrocarbons in the car's exhaust air. A common scheme involves the treatment of the original exhaust air in such a fashion as to assure the burning of all fuel vapors passing through the engine.

In the light of the damage caused by carbon monoxide and particularly the hydrocarbons, it appears that steps to reduce them can be nothing but beneficial, but doubts have been raised.

Donald E. Carr,* a research chemist, is not convinced. He cites the opinion of the distinguished chemist Philip Leighton of Stanford University, an authority on photochemistry. It should be recalled that, in the presence of sunlight, the hydrocarbons and nitrogen oxides from motor cars react to produce a great variety of other substances. Carr states the opinion that a substantial reduction of the hydrocarbons without a simultaneous reduction of nitrogen oxides could conceivably lead to such increased con-

* D. E. Carr, *The Breath of Life.* W. W. Norton (1965).

centrations of nitrogen dioxide that the danger to health and life might be increased rather than decreased. Obviously, many chemists disagree with this view. Provisions have been made for installing hydrocarbon-reducing devices on new cars. It is anticipated that, in the not too distant future, there will be more widespread legislative action on the state and federal levels requiring that all cars contain devices to reduce the quantities of unburned fuel blown into the atmosphere.

There is no assurance that this kind of regulation will solve the problem. In the long run, with population increasing at a staggering rate, there is a growing chorus of cries that, in cities at least, a means must be found to reduce the number of vehicles consuming petroleum products. Donald Carr, Morris Neiburger, Professor of Meteorology at the University of California at Los Angeles, and others as well, have proposed the widespread use of electric cars. Carr makes a case for the practicality of such automobiles for city driving, where small distances and low speeds are involved. But he probably is right when he regards the acceptance of this idea unlikely.

One step that has been taken by some (but not nearly enough) communities is the improvement of public transportation facilities. How much better an electrically operated subway or train than thousands of automobiles each containing one or two commuters! Why not more high-speed, electrically powered monorails? When considering the costs involved in building these systems of transportation and others in the same class, how much should you figure that cleaner air is worth? Without a doubt it has a large value when measured in dollars; it has an immeasurably higher value when measured in terms of health and life.

The time is long past when a city shrouded in potentially toxic gases, showered with the particles of soot and dust from its chimneys, can decide for or against improved public transport solely on the basis of construction and operation costs versus cash customers. The indirect benefits, as reflected in better health and greater beauty, those things which make life worth living, must be rated in such decisions. More people must be moved with less smoke, or the greater quantities of smoke will surely lead to fewer people.

SUGGESTED READING

P. L. Magill, F. R. Holden, and C. Ackley, eds., *Air Pollution Handbook.* New York: McGraw-Hill Book Co. (1956).

A. C. Stern, ed., *Air Pollution,* Vols. I and II. New York: Academic Press (1962).

C. E. Junge, *Air Chemistry and Radioactivity.* New York: Academic Press (1963).

W. L. Faith, *Air Pollution Control.* New York: John Wiley & Sons (1959).

D. E. Carr, *The Breath of Life,* W. W. Norton & Company (1965).

Air Conservation, by the Air Conservation Commission of the American Association for the Advancement of Science, Washington, D.C. (1966).

Note: The first three titles listed above are at an advanced technical level and serve as excellent reference books.

INDEX

INDEX

ANCHOR BOOKS

SCIENCE STUDY SERIES

17Ba

ANCHOR BOOKS

SCIENCE AND MATHEMATICS

AN APPROACH TO MODERN PHYSICS—E. N. Andrade, A111
THE BROKEN IMAGE: MAN, SCIENCE, AND SOCIETY—Floyd W. Matson, A506
DARWIN, MARX, WAGNER—Jacques Barzun, A127
DARWIN'S CENTURY—Loren Eiseley, A244
DISCOVERIES AND OPINIONS OF GALILEO—Stillman Drake, trans., A94
GIVE AND TAKE: The Biology of Tissue Transplantation—Francis D. Moore, A481
THE GREAT DOCTORS—Henry Sigerist, A140
HERRING GULL'S WORLD—A Study of the Social Behavior of Birds—Niko Tinbergen, A567
HOW TO SOLVE IT—G. Polya, A93
THE LANGUAGE OF LIFE—An Introduction to the Science of Genetics—George and Muriel Beadle, A579
THE LANGUAGE OF NATURE: An Essay on the Philosophy of Science—David Hawkins, A563
MEDIEVAL AND EARLY MODERN SCIENCE, Vol. I—A. C. Crombie, A167a
MEDIEVAL AND EARLY MODERN SCIENCE, Vol. II—A. C. Crombie, A167b
THE METAPHYSICAL FOUNDATIONS OF MODERN SCIENCE—Edwin Arthur Burtt, A41
MIRAGE OF HEALTH—René Dubos, A258
MODERN SCIENCE AND MODERN MAN—James B. Conant, A10
NUMBER, THE LANGUAGE OF SCIENCE—Tobias Dantzig, A67
RESEARCH PROBLEMS IN BIOLOGY: Investigations for Students—Biological Sciences Curriculum Study, Series 1, A366a
RESEARCH PROBLEMS IN BIOLOGY: Investigations for Students—Biological Sciences Curriculum Study, Series 2, A366b
RESEARCH PROBLEMS IN BIOLOGY: Investigations for Students—Biological Sciences Curriculum Study, Series 3, A366c
RESEARCH PROBLEMS IN BIOLOGY: Investigations for Students—Biological Sciences Curriculum Study, Series 4, A366d
A SHORT HISTORY OF SCIENCE—Herbert Butterfield and others, A180
STORY OF ENGINEERING—James Kip Finch, A214
UNITY OF THE UNIVERSE—D. W. Sciama, A247

ANCHOR BOOKS

NATURAL HISTORY LIBRARY

ANIMAL BEHAVIOR—John Paul Scott, N29
AUSTRALIAN ABORIGINES—A. P. Elkin, N37
BACK OF HISTORY, Revised edition—William Howells, N34
CELLS: THEIR STRUCTURE AND FUNCTION, Revised Edition—E. H. Mercer, N25
CHARLES DARWIN—Gavin de Beer, N41
EARLY MAN IN THE NEW WORLD—Kenneth Macgowan and Joseph A. Hester, N22
EXPLORATION OF THE COLORADO RIVER—John Wesley Powell, N11
FOREST PEOPLE—Colin Turnbull, N27
FROM FISH TO PHILOSOPHER—Homer W. Smith, N10
GENETICS—H. Kalmus, N38
A GUIDE TO BIRD WATCHING—Joseph J. Hickey, N30
HEATHENS—William Howells, N19
HERD OF RED DEER—F. Fraser Darling, N35
HORSES—George G. Simpson, N1
HOW TO MAKE A TELESCOPE—Jean Texereau, N31
INDIANS OF THE UNITED STATES—Clark Wissler, N42
LAND OF LITTLE RAIN—Mary Austin, A15
MARKETS IN AFRICA: Eight Subsistence Economies in Transition —Paul J. Bohannan and George Dalton, eds., N39
MODERN SCIENCE AND THE NATURE OF LIFE—William S. Beck, N8
MOUNTAINS OF CALIFORNIA—John Muir, N12
A NATURALIST IN ALASKA—Adolph Murie, N32
NAVAHO—Clyde Kluckhohn and Dorothea Leighton, N28
PACIFIC ISLANDS, Revised edition—Douglas Oliver, N14
RETURN TO LAUGHTER—Laura Marie Bohannan, N36
THE RUN—John Hay, N40
UNDER THE ANCESTORS' SHADOW—Kinship, Personality and Social Mobility in Village China—Francis L. K. Hsu, N43
VOYAGE OF THE BEAGLE—Charles Darwin, N16
YOSEMITE—John Muir, N26

ANCHOR BOOKS

CHEMISTRY IN ACTION SERIES

CHEMICALS FROM FERMENTATION—Peter A. Hahn, AMC3
CHEMICAL ENGINEERING—David H. Killeffer, AMC1
SILICA AND ME—Guy Alexander, AMC2
WATER IS EVERYBODY'S BUSINESS: The Chemistry of Water Purification—A. S. Behrman, AMC4